THIS Intermittent Fasting JOURNAL AND TRACKER IS DESIGNED TO HELP You CRUSH ALL YOUR health and wellness goals RELATED TO FASTING, WHETHER IT BE FOR weight loss, autophagy, aging, OR ALL THE many other benefits THAT COME WITH INTERMITTENT FASTING.

In this journal you can..

TRACK DAILY FASTS FOR AN ENTIRE YEAR

LOG YOUR MOODS

KEEP TRACK OF YOUR WATER INTAKE

WEEKLY BODY MEASUREMENTS

LOG WEIGHT LOSS, GAIN, OR MAINTENANCE

RECORD STRUGGLES & VICTORIES WITH EXTRA SPACE FOR

PERSONAL NOTES

AND FIND INSPIRATIONAL QUOTES TO REFLECT ON WEEKLY

Daily Fasting Tracker

	1AM	2AM	3AM	4AM	5AM	6AM	7AM	8AM	9AM	10AM	11AM	12PM	1PM	2PM	3PM	4PM	5PM	6PM	7PM	8PM	9PM	10PM	11PM	12AM
Monday	○	○	○	○	○	○	○	○	○	○	○	○	○	○	○	○	○	○	○	○	○	○	○	○
Tuesday	○	○	○	○	○	○	○	○	○	○	○	○	○	○	○	○	○	○	○	○	○	○	○	○
Wednesday	○	○	○	○	○	○	○	○	○	○	○	○	○	○	○	○	○	○	○	○	○	○	○	○
Thursday	○	○	○	○	○	○	○	○	○	○	○	○	○	○	○	○	○	○	○	○	○	○	○	○
Friday	○	○	○	○	○	○	○	○	○	○	○	○	○	○	○	○	○	○	○	○	○	○	○	○
Saturday	○	○	○	○	○	○	○	○	○	○	○	○	○	○	○	○	○	○	○	○	○	○	○	○
Sunday	○	○	○	○	○	○	○	○	○	○	○	○	○	○	○	○	○	○	○	○	○	○	○	○

Mood

MON
TUE
WED
THU
FRI
SAT
SUN

Daily Water Log

MON
TUES
WED
THU
FRI
SAT
SUN

Weekly Tally & Notes

Body Measurements:

BUST _____
UPPER ARM _____
WAIST _____
HIPS _____
UPPER LEG _____

Weekly Weight Tracker

CURRENT WEIGHT _____
GOAL WEIGHT _____

STRUGGLES

VICTORIES

Notes:

bust

upper arm _____

waist

hips

upper leg _____

Set goals and crush them.

Daily Fasting Tracker

	1AM	2AM	3AM	4AM	5AM	6AM	7AM	8AM	9AM	10AM	11AM	12PM	1PM	2PM	3PM	4PM	5PM	6PM	7PM	8PM	9PM	10PM	11PM	12AM
Monday	○	○	○	○	○	○	○	○	○	○	○	○	○	○	○	○	○	○	○	○	○	○	○	○
Tuesday	○	○	○	○	○	○	○	○	○	○	○	○	○	○	○	○	○	○	○	○	○	○	○	○
Wednesday	○	○	○	○	○	○	○	○	○	○	○	○	○	○	○	○	○	○	○	○	○	○	○	○
Thursday	○	○	○	○	○	○	○	○	○	○	○	○	○	○	○	○	○	○	○	○	○	○	○	○
Friday	○	○	○	○	○	○	○	○	○	○	○	○	○	○	○	○	○	○	○	○	○	○	○	○
Saturday	○	○	○	○	○	○	○	○	○	○	○	○	○	○	○	○	○	○	○	○	○	○	○	○
Sunday	○	○	○	○	○	○	○	○	○	○	○	○	○	○	○	○	○	○	○	○	○	○	○	○

Mood

MON
TUE
WED
THU
FRI
SAT
SUN

Daily Water Log

MON
TUES
WED
THU
FRI
SAT
SUN

Weekly Tally & Notes

Body Measurements:

bust ———— upper arm ————

waist ————

———— hips

upper leg ————

BUST	———
UPPER ARM	———
WAIST	———
HIPS	———
UPPER LEG	———

Weekly Weight Tracker

CURRENT WEIGHT ———
GOAL WEIGHT ———

STRUGGLES

VICTORIES

Notes:

Take a step towards the person you want to be.

Daily Fasting Tracker

	1AM	2AM	3AM	4AM	5AM	6AM	7AM	8AM	9AM	10AM	11AM	12PM	1PM	2PM	3PM	4PM	5PM	6PM	7PM	8PM	9PM	10PM	11PM	12AM
Monday	○	○	○	○	○	○	○	○	○	○	○	○	○	○	○	○	○	○	○	○	○	○	○	○
Tuesday	○	○	○	○	○	○	○	○	○	○	○	○	○	○	○	○	○	○	○	○	○	○	○	○
Wednesday	○	○	○	○	○	○	○	○	○	○	○	○	○	○	○	○	○	○	○	○	○	○	○	○
Thursday	○	○	○	○	○	○	○	○	○	○	○	○	○	○	○	○	○	○	○	○	○	○	○	○
Friday	○	○	○	○	○	○	○	○	○	○	○	○	○	○	○	○	○	○	○	○	○	○	○	○
Saturday	○	○	○	○	○	○	○	○	○	○	○	○	○	○	○	○	○	○	○	○	○	○	○	○
Sunday	○	○	○	○	○	○	○	○	○	○	○	○	○	○	○	○	○	○	○	○	○	○	○	○

Mood

MON
TUE
WED
THU
FRI
SAT
SUN

Daily Water Log

MON	◇ ◇ ◇ ◇ ◇ ◇ ◇ ◇
TUES	◇ ◇ ◇ ◇ ◇ ◇ ◇ ◇
WED	◇ ◇ ◇ ◇ ◇ ◇ ◇ ◇
THU	◇ ◇ ◇ ◇ ◇ ◇ ◇ ◇
FRI	◇ ◇ ◇ ◇ ◇ ◇ ◇ ◇
SAT	◇ ◇ ◇ ◇ ◇ ◇ ◇ ◇
SUN	◇ ◇ ◇ ◇ ◇ ◇ ◇ ◇

Weekly Tally & Notes

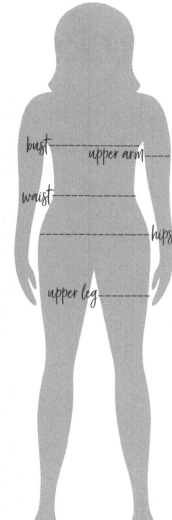

Body Measurements:

BUST _____
UPPER ARM _____
WAIST _____
HIPS _____
UPPER LEG _____

Weekly Weight Tracker

CURRENT WEIGHT _____
GOAL WEIGHT _____

STRUGGLES

VICTORIES

Notes:

If you can't stop thinking about it, don't stop working for it.

Daily Fasting Tracker

	1AM	2AM	3AM	4AM	5AM	6AM	7AM	8AM	9AM	10AM	11AM	12PM	1PM	2PM	3PM	4PM	5PM	6PM	7PM	8PM	9PM	10PM	11PM	12AM
Monday	○	○	○	○	○	○	○	○	○	○	○	○	○	○	○	○	○	○	○	○	○	○	○	○
Tuesday	○	○	○	○	○	○	○	○	○	○	○	○	○	○	○	○	○	○	○	○	○	○	○	○
Wednesday	○	○	○	○	○	○	○	○	○	○	○	○	○	○	○	○	○	○	○	○	○	○	○	○
Thursday	○	○	○	○	○	○	○	○	○	○	○	○	○	○	○	○	○	○	○	○	○	○	○	○
Friday	○	○	○	○	○	○	○	○	○	○	○	○	○	○	○	○	○	○	○	○	○	○	○	○
Saturday	○	○	○	○	○	○	○	○	○	○	○	○	○	○	○	○	○	○	○	○	○	○	○	○
Sunday	○	○	○	○	○	○	○	○	○	○	○	○	○	○	○	○	○	○	○	○	○	○	○	○

Mood

MON
TUE
WED
THU
FRI
SAT
SUN

Daily Water Log

MON	◇ ◇ ◇ ◇ ◇ ◇ ◇ ◇
TUES	◇ ◇ ◇ ◇ ◇ ◇ ◇ ◇
WED	◇ ◇ ◇ ◇ ◇ ◇ ◇ ◇
THU	◇ ◇ ◇ ◇ ◇ ◇ ◇ ◇
FRI	◇ ◇ ◇ ◇ ◇ ◇ ◇ ◇
SAT	◇ ◇ ◇ ◇ ◇ ◇ ◇ ◇
SUN	◇ ◇ ◇ ◇ ◇ ◇ ◇ ◇

Weekly Tally & Notes

Body Measurements:

BUST _____
UPPER ARM _____
WAIST _____
HIPS _____
UPPER LEG _____

Weekly Weight Tracker

CURRENT WEIGHT _____
GOAL WEIGHT _____

STRUGGLES

VICTORIES

Notes:

bust ——————
upper arm ————
waist ——————
hips
upper leg ————

Be Focused. Be Persistent. Never Quit

Daily Fasting Tracker

	1AM	2AM	3AM	4AM	5AM	6AM	7AM	8AM	9AM	10AM	11AM	12PM	1PM	2PM	3PM	4PM	5PM	6PM	7PM	8PM	9PM	10PM	11PM	12AM
Monday	○	○	○	○	○	○	○	○	○	○	○	○	○	○	○	○	○	○	○	○	○	○	○	○
Tuesday	○	○	○	○	○	○	○	○	○	○	○	○	○	○	○	○	○	○	○	○	○	○	○	○
Wednesday	○	○	○	○	○	○	○	○	○	○	○	○	○	○	○	○	○	○	○	○	○	○	○	○
Thursday	○	○	○	○	○	○	○	○	○	○	○	○	○	○	○	○	○	○	○	○	○	○	○	○
Friday	○	○	○	○	○	○	○	○	○	○	○	○	○	○	○	○	○	○	○	○	○	○	○	○
Saturday	○	○	○	○	○	○	○	○	○	○	○	○	○	○	○	○	○	○	○	○	○	○	○	○
Sunday	○	○	○	○	○	○	○	○	○	○	○	○	○	○	○	○	○	○	○	○	○	○	○	○

Mood

MON

TUE

WED

THU

FRI

SAT

SUN

Daily Water Log

MON ⬡ ⬡ ⬡ ⬡ ⬡ ⬡ ⬡ ⬡

TUES ⬡ ⬡ ⬡ ⬡ ⬡ ⬡ ⬡ ⬡

WED ⬡ ⬡ ⬡ ⬡ ⬡ ⬡ ⬡ ⬡

THU ⬡ ⬡ ⬡ ⬡ ⬡ ⬡ ⬡ ⬡

FRI ⬡ ⬡ ⬡ ⬡ ⬡ ⬡ ⬡ ⬡

SAT ⬡ ⬡ ⬡ ⬡ ⬡ ⬡ ⬡ ⬡

SUN ⬡ ⬡ ⬡ ⬡ ⬡ ⬡ ⬡ ⬡

Weekly Tally & Notes

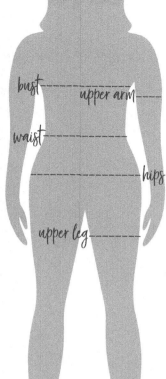

bust — — — —
upper arm — — —
waist — — — —
hips — — —
upper leg — — — —

Body Measurements:

BUST _____
UPPER ARM _____
WAIST _____
HIPS _____
UPPER LEG _____

Weekly Weight Tracker

CURRENT WEIGHT _____
GOAL WEIGHT _____

STRUGGLES

VICTORIES

Notes:

There are seven days in a week and someday isn't one of them.

Daily Fasting Tracker

	1AM	2AM	3AM	4AM	5AM	6AM	7AM	8AM	9AM	10AM	11AM	12PM	1PM	2PM	3PM	4PM	5PM	6PM	7PM	8PM	9PM	10PM	11PM	12AM
Monday	○	○	○	○	○	○	○	○	○	○	○	○	○	○	○	○	○	○	○	○	○	○	○	○
Tuesday	○	○	○	○	○	○	○	○	○	○	○	○	○	○	○	○	○	○	○	○	○	○	○	○
Wednesday	○	○	○	○	○	○	○	○	○	○	○	○	○	○	○	○	○	○	○	○	○	○	○	○
Thursday	○	○	○	○	○	○	○	○	○	○	○	○	○	○	○	○	○	○	○	○	○	○	○	○
Friday	○	○	○	○	○	○	○	○	○	○	○	○	○	○	○	○	○	○	○	○	○	○	○	○
Saturday	○	○	○	○	○	○	○	○	○	○	○	○	○	○	○	○	○	○	○	○	○	○	○	○
Sunday	○	○	○	○	○	○	○	○	○	○	○	○	○	○	○	○	○	○	○	○	○	○	○	○

Mood

MON
TUE
WED
THU
FRI
SAT
SUN

Daily Water Log

MON	◊ ◊ ◊ ◊ ◊ ◊ ◊ ◊
TUES	◊ ◊ ◊ ◊ ◊ ◊ ◊ ◊
WED	◊ ◊ ◊ ◊ ◊ ◊ ◊ ◊
THU	◊ ◊ ◊ ◊ ◊ ◊ ◊ ◊
FRI	◊ ◊ ◊ ◊ ◊ ◊ ◊ ◊
SAT	◊ ◊ ◊ ◊ ◊ ◊ ◊ ◊
SUN	◊ ◊ ◊ ◊ ◊ ◊ ◊ ◊

Weekly Tally & Notes

bust
upper arm
waist
hips
upper leg

Body Measurements:

BUST _____
UPPER ARM _____
WAIST _____
HIPS _____
UPPER LEG _____

Weekly Weight Tracker

CURRENT WEIGHT _____
GOAL WEIGHT _____

STRUGGLES

VICTORIES

Notes:

Dream big. Work hard. Make it happen.

Daily Fasting Tracker

	1AM	2AM	3AM	4AM	5AM	6AM	7AM	8AM	9AM	10AM	11AM	12PM	1PM	2PM	3PM	4PM	5PM	6PM	7PM	8PM	9PM	10PM	11PM	12AM
Monday	○	○	○	○	○	○	○	○	○	○	○	○	○	○	○	○	○	○	○	○	○	○	○	○
Tuesday	○	○	○	○	○	○	○	○	○	○	○	○	○	○	○	○	○	○	○	○	○	○	○	○
Wednesday	○	○	○	○	○	○	○	○	○	○	○	○	○	○	○	○	○	○	○	○	○	○	○	○
Thursday	○	○	○	○	○	○	○	○	○	○	○	○	○	○	○	○	○	○	○	○	○	○	○	○
Friday	○	○	○	○	○	○	○	○	○	○	○	○	○	○	○	○	○	○	○	○	○	○	○	○
Saturday	○	○	○	○	○	○	○	○	○	○	○	○	○	○	○	○	○	○	○	○	○	○	○	○
Sunday	○	○	○	○	○	○	○	○	○	○	○	○	○	○	○	○	○	○	○	○	○	○	○	○

Mood

MON
TUE
WED
THU
FRI
SAT
SUN

Daily Water Log

MON
TUES
WED
THU
FRI
SAT
SUN

Weekly Tally & Notes

Body Measurements:

BUST	_____
UPPER ARM	_____
WAIST	_____
HIPS	_____
UPPER LEG	_____

Weekly Weight Tracker

CURRENT WEIGHT	_____
GOAL WEIGHT	_____

STRUGGLES

VICTORIES

Notes:

bust

upper arm

waist

hips

upper leg

You only fail if you give up.

Daily Fasting Tracker

	1AM	2AM	3AM	4AM	5AM	6AM	7AM	8AM	9AM	10AM	11AM	12PM	1PM	2PM	3PM	4PM	5PM	6PM	7PM	8PM	9PM	10PM	11PM	12AM
Monday	○	○	○	○	○	○	○	○	○	○	○	○	○	○	○	○	○	○	○	○	○	○	○	○
Tuesday	○	○	○	○	○	○	○	○	○	○	○	○	○	○	○	○	○	○	○	○	○	○	○	○
Wednesday	○	○	○	○	○	○	○	○	○	○	○	○	○	○	○	○	○	○	○	○	○	○	○	○
Thursday	○	○	○	○	○	○	○	○	○	○	○	○	○	○	○	○	○	○	○	○	○	○	○	○
Friday	○	○	○	○	○	○	○	○	○	○	○	○	○	○	○	○	○	○	○	○	○	○	○	○
Saturday	○	○	○	○	○	○	○	○	○	○	○	○	○	○	○	○	○	○	○	○	○	○	○	○
Sunday	○	○	○	○	○	○	○	○	○	○	○	○	○	○	○	○	○	○	○	○	○	○	○	○

Mood

MON
TUE
WED
THU
FRI
SAT
SUN

Daily Water Log

MON	🛆 🛆 🛆 🛆 🛆 🛆 🛆 🛆
TUES	🛆 🛆 🛆 🛆 🛆 🛆 🛆 🛆
WED	🛆 🛆 🛆 🛆 🛆 🛆 🛆 🛆
THU	🛆 🛆 🛆 🛆 🛆 🛆 🛆 🛆
FRI	🛆 🛆 🛆 🛆 🛆 🛆 🛆 🛆
SAT	🛆 🛆 🛆 🛆 🛆 🛆 🛆 🛆
SUN	🛆 🛆 🛆 🛆 🛆 🛆 🛆 🛆

Weekly Tally & Notes

Body Measurements:

BUST _____
UPPER ARM _____
WAIST _____
HIPS _____
UPPER LEG _____

Weekly Weight Tracker

CURRENT WEIGHT _____
GOAL WEIGHT _____

bust ——————— upper arm ———
waist ———————————
——————— hips
upper leg ———————

STRUGGLES

VICTORIES

Notes:

You are entirely up to you.

Daily Fasting Tracker

	1AM	2AM	3AM	4AM	5AM	6AM	7AM	8AM	9AM	10AM	11AM	12PM	1PM	2PM	3PM	4PM	5PM	6PM	7PM	8PM	9PM	10PM	11PM	12AM
Monday	○	○	○	○	○	○	○	○	○	○	○	○	○	○	○	○	○	○	○	○	○	○	○	○
Tuesday	○	○	○	○	○	○	○	○	○	○	○	○	○	○	○	○	○	○	○	○	○	○	○	○
Wednesday	○	○	○	○	○	○	○	○	○	○	○	○	○	○	○	○	○	○	○	○	○	○	○	○
Thursday	○	○	○	○	○	○	○	○	○	○	○	○	○	○	○	○	○	○	○	○	○	○	○	○
Friday	○	○	○	○	○	○	○	○	○	○	○	○	○	○	○	○	○	○	○	○	○	○	○	○
Saturday	○	○	○	○	○	○	○	○	○	○	○	○	○	○	○	○	○	○	○	○	○	○	○	○
Sunday	○	○	○	○	○	○	○	○	○	○	○	○	○	○	○	○	○	○	○	○	○	○	○	○

Mood

MON
TUE
WED
THU
FRI
SAT
SUN

Daily Water Log

MON
TUES
WED
THU
FRI
SAT
SUN

Weekly Tally & Notes

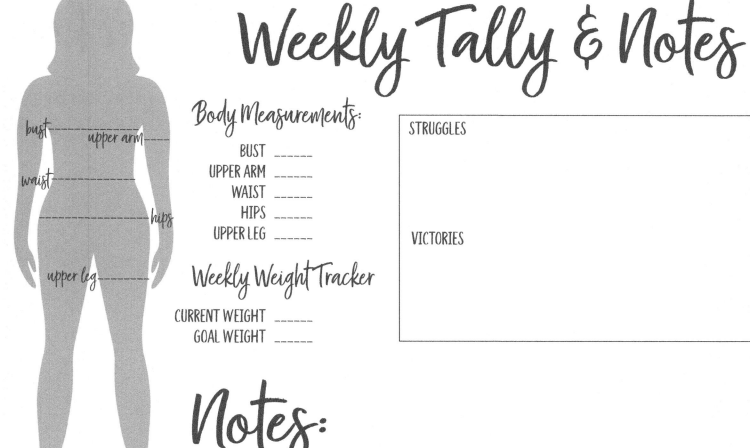

Body Measurements:

BUST _____
UPPER ARM _____
WAIST _____
HIPS _____
UPPER LEG _____

Weekly Weight Tracker

CURRENT WEIGHT _____
GOAL WEIGHT _____

STRUGGLES

VICTORIES

Notes:

Doubt kills more dreams than failure ever will.

Daily Fasting Tracker

	1AM	2AM	3AM	4AM	5AM	6AM	7AM	8AM	9AM	10AM	11AM	12PM	1PM	2PM	3PM	4PM	5PM	6PM	7PM	8PM	9PM	10PM	11PM	12AM
Monday	○	○	○	○	○	○	○	○	○	○	○	○	○	○	○	○	○	○	○	○	○	○	○	○
Tuesday	○	○	○	○	○	○	○	○	○	○	○	○	○	○	○	○	○	○	○	○	○	○	○	○
Wednesday	○	○	○	○	○	○	○	○	○	○	○	○	○	○	○	○	○	○	○	○	○	○	○	○
Thursday	○	○	○	○	○	○	○	○	○	○	○	○	○	○	○	○	○	○	○	○	○	○	○	○
Friday	○	○	○	○	○	○	○	○	○	○	○	○	○	○	○	○	○	○	○	○	○	○	○	○
Saturday	○	○	○	○	○	○	○	○	○	○	○	○	○	○	○	○	○	○	○	○	○	○	○	○
Sunday	○	○	○	○	○	○	○	○	○	○	○	○	○	○	○	○	○	○	○	○	○	○	○	○

Mood

MON
TUE
WED
THU
FRI
SAT
SUN

Daily Water Log

MON	△ △ △ △ △ △ △ △
TUES	△ △ △ △ △ △ △ △
WED	△ △ △ △ △ △ △ △
THU	△ △ △ △ △ △ △ △
FRI	△ △ △ △ △ △ △ △
SAT	△ △ △ △ △ △ △ △
SUN	△ △ △ △ △ △ △ △

Weekly Tally & Notes

Body Measurements:

bust

upper arm

waist

hips

upper leg

BUST _____
UPPER ARM _____
WAIST _____
HIPS _____
UPPER LEG _____

Weekly Weight Tracker

CURRENT WEIGHT _____
GOAL WEIGHT _____

STRUGGLES

VICTORIES

Notes:

Be you. Do you. For you.

Daily Fasting Tracker

	1AM	2AM	3AM	4AM	5AM	6AM	7AM	8AM	9AM	10AM	11AM	12PM	1PM	2PM	3PM	4PM	5PM	6PM	7PM	8PM	9PM	10PM	11PM	12AM
Monday	○	○	○	○	○	○	○	○	○	○	○	○	○	○	○	○	○	○	○	○	○	○	○	○
Tuesday	○	○	○	○	○	○	○	○	○	○	○	○	○	○	○	○	○	○	○	○	○	○	○	○
Wednesday	○	○	○	○	○	○	○	○	○	○	○	○	○	○	○	○	○	○	○	○	○	○	○	○
Thursday	○	○	○	○	○	○	○	○	○	○	○	○	○	○	○	○	○	○	○	○	○	○	○	○
Friday	○	○	○	○	○	○	○	○	○	○	○	○	○	○	○	○	○	○	○	○	○	○	○	○
Saturday	○	○	○	○	○	○	○	○	○	○	○	○	○	○	○	○	○	○	○	○	○	○	○	○
Sunday	○	○	○	○	○	○	○	○	○	○	○	○	○	○	○	○	○	○	○	○	○	○	○	○

Mood

MON
TUE
WED
THU
FRI
SAT
SUN

Daily Water Log

MON
TUES
WED
THU
FRI
SAT
SUN

Weekly Tally & Notes

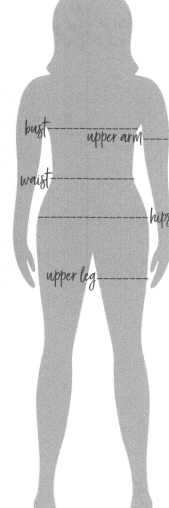

Body Measurements:

BUST	_____
UPPER ARM	_____
WAIST	_____
HIPS	_____
UPPER LEG	_____

Weekly Weight Tracker

CURRENT WEIGHT	_____
GOAL WEIGHT	_____

STRUGGLES

VICTORIES

Notes:

Never let a stumble in the road be the end of the journey.

Daily Fasting Tracker

	1AM	2AM	3AM	4AM	5AM	6AM	7AM	8AM	9AM	10AM	11AM	12PM	1PM	2PM	3PM	4PM	5PM	6PM	7PM	8PM	9PM	10PM	11PM	12AM
Monday	○	○	○	○	○	○	○	○	○	○	○	○	○	○	○	○	○	○	○	○	○	○	○	○
Tuesday	○	○	○	○	○	○	○	○	○	○	○	○	○	○	○	○	○	○	○	○	○	○	○	○
Wednesday	○	○	○	○	○	○	○	○	○	○	○	○	○	○	○	○	○	○	○	○	○	○	○	○
Thursday	○	○	○	○	○	○	○	○	○	○	○	○	○	○	○	○	○	○	○	○	○	○	○	○
Friday	○	○	○	○	○	○	○	○	○	○	○	○	○	○	○	○	○	○	○	○	○	○	○	○
Saturday	○	○	○	○	○	○	○	○	○	○	○	○	○	○	○	○	○	○	○	○	○	○	○	○
Sunday	○	○	○	○	○	○	○	○	○	○	○	○	○	○	○	○	○	○	○	○	○	○	○	○

Mood

MON
TUE
WED
THU
FRI
SAT
SUN

Daily Water Log

MON	○ ○ ○ ○ ○ ○ ○ ○
TUES	○ ○ ○ ○ ○ ○ ○ ○
WED	○ ○ ○ ○ ○ ○ ○ ○
THU	○ ○ ○ ○ ○ ○ ○ ○
FRI	○ ○ ○ ○ ○ ○ ○ ○
SAT	○ ○ ○ ○ ○ ○ ○
SUN	○ ○ ○ ○ ○ ○ ○

Weekly Tally & Notes

Body image labels: bust, upper arm, waist, hips, upper leg

Body Measurements:

BUST _____
UPPER ARM _____
WAIST _____
HIPS _____
UPPER LEG _____

Weekly Weight Tracker

CURRENT WEIGHT _____
GOAL WEIGHT _____

STRUGGLES

VICTORIES

Notes:

The process might be slow, but quitting won't speed it up.

Daily Fasting Tracker

	1AM	2AM	3AM	4AM	5AM	6AM	7AM	8AM	9AM	10AM	11AM	12PM	1PM	2PM	3PM	4PM	5PM	6PM	7PM	8PM	9PM	10PM	11PM	12AM
Monday	○	○	○	○	○	○	○	○	○	○	○	○	○	○	○	○	○	○	○	○	○	○	○	○
Tuesday	○	○	○	○	○	○	○	○	○	○	○	○	○	○	○	○	○	○	○	○	○	○	○	○
Wednesday	○	○	○	○	○	○	○	○	○	○	○	○	○	○	○	○	○	○	○	○	○	○	○	○
Thursday	○	○	○	○	○	○	○	○	○	○	○	○	○	○	○	○	○	○	○	○	○	○	○	○
Friday	○	○	○	○	○	○	○	○	○	○	○	○	○	○	○	○	○	○	○	○	○	○	○	○
Saturday	○	○	○	○	○	○	○	○	○	○	○	○	○	○	○	○	○	○	○	○	○	○	○	○
Sunday	○	○	○	○	○	○	○	○	○	○	○	○	○	○	○	○	○	○	○	○	○	○	○	○

Mood

MON
TUE
WED
THU
FRI
SAT
SUN

Daily Water Log

MON	○ ○ ○ ○ ○ ○ ○ ○
TUES	○ ○ ○ ○ ○ ○ ○ ○
WED	○ ○ ○ ○ ○ ○ ○ ○
THU	○ ○ ○ ○ ○ ○ ○ ○
FRI	○ ○ ○ ○ ○ ○ ○ ○
SAT	○ ○ ○ ○ ○ ○ ○ ○
SUN	○ ○ ○ ○ ○ ○ ○ ○

Weekly Tally & Notes

Body Measurements:

BUST	_____
UPPER ARM	_____
WAIST	_____
HIPS	_____
UPPER LEG	_____

Weekly Weight Tracker

CURRENT WEIGHT	_____
GOAL WEIGHT	_____

STRUGGLES

VICTORIES

Notes:

bust

upper arm

waist

hips

upper leg

Believe in the person you want to become.

Daily Fasting Tracker

	1AM	2AM	3AM	4AM	5AM	6AM	7AM	8AM	9AM	10AM	11AM	12PM	1PM	2PM	3PM	4PM	5PM	6PM	7PM	8PM	9PM	10PM	11PM	12AM
Monday	○	○	○	○	○	○	○	○	○	○	○	○	○	○	○	○	○	○	○	○	○	○	○	○
Tuesday	○	○	○	○	○	○	○	○	○	○	○	○	○	○	○	○	○	○	○	○	○	○	○	○
Wednesday	○	○	○	○	○	○	○	○	○	○	○	○	○	○	○	○	○	○	○	○	○	○	○	○
Thursday	○	○	○	○	○	○	○	○	○	○	○	○	○	○	○	○	○	○	○	○	○	○	○	○
Friday	○	○	○	○	○	○	○	○	○	○	○	○	○	○	○	○	○	○	○	○	○	○	○	○
Saturday	○	○	○	○	○	○	○	○	○	○	○	○	○	○	○	○	○	○	○	○	○	○	○	○
Sunday	○	○	○	○	○	○	○	○	○	○	○	○	○	○	○	○	○	○	○	○	○	○	○	○

Mood

Daily Water Log

MON	⬦ ⬦ ⬦ ⬦ ⬦ ⬦ ⬦ ⬦
TUES	⬦ ⬦ ⬦ ⬦ ⬦ ⬦ ⬦ ⬦
WED	⬦ ⬦ ⬦ ⬦ ⬦ ⬦ ⬦ ⬦
THU	⬦ ⬦ ⬦ ⬦ ⬦ ⬦ ⬦ ⬦
FRI	⬦ ⬦ ⬦ ⬦ ⬦ ⬦ ⬦ ⬦
SAT	⬦ ⬦ ⬦ ⬦ ⬦ ⬦ ⬦ ⬦
SUN	⬦ ⬦ ⬦ ⬦ ⬦ ⬦ ⬦ ⬦

Weekly Tally & Notes

Body Measurements:

BUST _____
UPPER ARM _____
WAIST _____
HIPS _____
UPPER LEG _____

Weekly Weight Tracker

CURRENT WEIGHT _____
GOAL WEIGHT _____

bust ----------
upper arm ------
waist ----------
hips ----------
upper leg ----------

STRUGGLES

VICTORIES

Notes:

No grit, no pearl.

Daily Fasting Tracker

	1AM	2AM	3AM	4AM	5AM	6AM	7AM	8AM	9AM	10AM	11AM	12PM	1PM	2PM	3PM	4PM	5PM	6PM	7PM	8PM	9PM	10PM	11PM	12AM
Monday	○	○	○	○	○	○	○	○	○	○	○	○	○	○	○	○	○	○	○	○	○	○	○	○
Tuesday	○	○	○	○	○	○	○	○	○	○	○	○	○	○	○	○	○	○	○	○	○	○	○	○
Wednesday	○	○	○	○	○	○	○	○	○	○	○	○	○	○	○	○	○	○	○	○	○	○	○	○
Thursday	○	○	○	○	○	○	○	○	○	○	○	○	○	○	○	○	○	○	○	○	○	○	○	○
Friday	○	○	○	○	○	○	○	○	○	○	○	○	○	○	○	○	○	○	○	○	○	○	○	○
Saturday	○	○	○	○	○	○	○	○	○	○	○	○	○	○	○	○	○	○	○	○	○	○	○	○
Sunday	○	○	○	○	○	○	○	○	○	○	○	○	○	○	○	○	○	○	○	○	○	○	○	○

Mood

MON
TUE
WED
THU
FRI
SAT
SUN

Daily Water Log

MON	○ ○ ○ ○ ○ ○ ○ ○
TUES	○ ○ ○ ○ ○ ○ ○ ○
WED	○ ○ ○ ○ ○ ○ ○ ○
THU	○ ○ ○ ○ ○ ○ ○ ○
FRI	○ ○ ○ ○ ○ ○ ○ ○
SAT	○ ○ ○ ○ ○ ○ ○ ○
SUN	○ ○ ○ ○ ○ ○ ○ ○

Weekly Tally & Notes

Body Measurements:

BUST _____
UPPER ARM _____
WAIST _____
HIPS _____
UPPER LEG _____

Weekly Weight Tracker

CURRENT WEIGHT _____
GOAL WEIGHT _____

bust
upper arm
waist
hips
upper leg

STRUGGLES

VICTORIES

Notes:

Believe you can and you're halfway there.

Daily Fasting Tracker

	1AM	2AM	3AM	4AM	5AM	6AM	7AM	8AM	9AM	10AM	11AM	12PM	1PM	2PM	3PM	4PM	5PM	6PM	7PM	8PM	9PM	10PM	11PM	12AM
Monday	○	○	○	○	○	○	○	○	○	○	○	○	○	○	○	○	○	○	○	○	○	○	○	○
Tuesday	○	○	○	○	○	○	○	○	○	○	○	○	○	○	○	○	○	○	○	○	○	○	○	○
Wednesday	○	○	○	○	○	○	○	○	○	○	○	○	○	○	○	○	○	○	○	○	○	○	○	○
Thursday	○	○	○	○	○	○	○	○	○	○	○	○	○	○	○	○	○	○	○	○	○	○	○	○
Friday	○	○	○	○	○	○	○	○	○	○	○	○	○	○	○	○	○	○	○	○	○	○	○	○
Saturday	○	○	○	○	○	○	○	○	○	○	○	○	○	○	○	○	○	○	○	○	○	○	○	○
Sunday	○	○	○	○	○	○	○	○	○	○	○	○	○	○	○	○	○	○	○	○	○	○	○	○

Mood

MON
TUE
WED
THU
FRI
SAT
SUN

Daily Water Log

MON	◇ ◇ ◇ ◇ ◇ ◇ ◇ ◇
TUES	◇ ◇ ◇ ◇ ◇ ◇ ◇ ◇
WED	◇ ◇ ◇ ◇ ◇ ◇ ◇ ◇
THU	◇ ◇ ◇ ◇ ◇ ◇ ◇ ◇
FRI	◇ ◇ ◇ ◇ ◇ ◇ ◇ ◇
SAT	◇ ◇ ◇ ◇ ◇ ◇ ◇ ◇
SUN	◇ ◇ ◇ ◇ ◇ ◇ ◇ ◇

bust----------
upper arm------
waist----------------
------------hips
upper leg----------

Weekly Tally & Notes

Body Measurements:

BUST _____
UPPER ARM _____
WAIST _____
HIPS _____
UPPER LEG _____

Weekly Weight Tracker

CURRENT WEIGHT _____
GOAL WEIGHT _____

STRUGGLES

VICTORIES

Notes:

Love yourself.

Daily Fasting Tracker

	1AM	2AM	3AM	4AM	5AM	6AM	7AM	8AM	9AM	10AM	11AM	12PM	1PM	2PM	3PM	4PM	5PM	6PM	7PM	8PM	9PM	10PM	11PM	12AM
Monday	○	○	○	○	○	○	○	○	○	○	○	○	○	○	○	○	○	○	○	○	○	○	○	○
Tuesday	○	○	○	○	○	○	○	○	○	○	○	○	○	○	○	○	○	○	○	○	○	○	○	○
Wednesday	○	○	○	○	○	○	○	○	○	○	○	○	○	○	○	○	○	○	○	○	○	○	○	○
Thursday	○	○	○	○	○	○	○	○	○	○	○	○	○	○	○	○	○	○	○	○	○	○	○	○
Friday	○	○	○	○	○	○	○	○	○	○	○	○	○	○	○	○	○	○	○	○	○	○	○	○
Saturday	○	○	○	○	○	○	○	○	○	○	○	○	○	○	○	○	○	○	○	○	○	○	○	○
Sunday	○	○	○	○	○	○	○	○	○	○	○	○	○	○	○	○	○	○	○	○	○	○	○	○

Mood

MON

TUE

WED

THU

FRI

SAT

SUN

Daily Water Log

MON	◇ ◇ ◇ ◇ ◇ ◇ ◇ ◇
TUES	◇ ◇ ◇ ◇ ◇ ◇ ◇ ◇
WED	◇ ◇ ◇ ◇ ◇ ◇ ◇ ◇
THU	◇ ◇ ◇ ◇ ◇ ◇ ◇ ◇
FRI	◇ ◇ ◇ ◇ ◇ ◇ ◇ ◇
SAT	◇ ◇ ◇ ◇ ◇ ◇ ◇ ◇
SUN	◇ ◇ ◇ ◇ ◇ ◇ ◇ ◇

Weekly Tally & Notes

Body Measurements:

bust —————— upper arm ——————

waist ——————————

—————————— hips

upper leg ——————

BUST _____
UPPER ARM _____
WAIST _____
HIPS _____
UPPER LEG _____

Weekly Weight Tracker

CURRENT WEIGHT _____
GOAL WEIGHT _____

STRUGGLES

VICTORIES

Notes:

No pressure, no diamonds.

Daily Fasting Tracker

	1AM	2AM	3AM	4AM	5AM	6AM	7AM	8AM	9AM	10AM	11AM	12PM	1PM	2PM	3PM	4PM	5PM	6PM	7PM	8PM	9PM	10PM	11PM	12AM
Monday	○	○	○	○	○	○	○	○	○	○	○	○	○	○	○	○	○	○	○	○	○	○	○	○
Tuesday	○	○	○	○	○	○	○	○	○	○	○	○	○	○	○	○	○	○	○	○	○	○	○	○
Wednesday	○	○	○	○	○	○	○	○	○	○	○	○	○	○	○	○	○	○	○	○	○	○	○	○
Thursday	○	○	○	○	○	○	○	○	○	○	○	○	○	○	○	○	○	○	○	○	○	○	○	○
Friday	○	○	○	○	○	○	○	○	○	○	○	○	○	○	○	○	○	○	○	○	○	○	○	○
Saturday	○	○	○	○	○	○	○	○	○	○	○	○	○	○	○	○	○	○	○	○	○	○	○	○
Sunday	○	○	○	○	○	○	○	○	○	○	○	○	○	○	○	○	○	○	○	○	○	○	○	○

Mood

MON
TUE
WED
THU
FRI
SAT
SUN

Daily Water Log

MON	⬠ ⬠ ⬠ ⬠ ⬠ ⬠ ⬠ ⬠
TUES	⬠ ⬠ ⬠ ⬠ ⬠ ⬠ ⬠ ⬠
WED	⬠ ⬠ ⬠ ⬠ ⬠ ⬠ ⬠ ⬠
THU	⬠ ⬠ ⬠ ⬠ ⬠ ⬠ ⬠ ⬠
FRI	⬠ ⬠ ⬠ ⬠ ⬠ ⬠ ⬠ ⬠
SAT	⬠ ⬠ ⬠ ⬠ ⬠ ⬠ ⬠ ⬠
SUN	⬠ ⬠ ⬠ ⬠ ⬠ ⬠ ⬠ ⬠

Weekly Tally & Notes

Body Measurements:

bust ———————

upper arm ———————

waist ———————

hips ———————

upper leg ———————

BUST _____

UPPER ARM _____

WAIST _____

HIPS _____

UPPER LEG _____

Weekly Weight Tracker

CURRENT WEIGHT _____

GOAL WEIGHT _____

STRUGGLES

VICTORIES

Notes:

You can.

Daily Fasting Tracker

	1AM	2AM	3AM	4AM	5AM	6AM	7AM	8AM	9AM	10AM	11AM	12PM	1PM	2PM	3PM	4PM	5PM	6PM	7PM	8PM	9PM	10PM	11PM	12AM
Monday	○	○	○	○	○	○	○	○	○	○	○	○	○	○	○	○	○	○	○	○	○	○	○	○
Tuesday	○	○	○	○	○	○	○	○	○	○	○	○	○	○	○	○	○	○	○	○	○	○	○	○
Wednesday	○	○	○	○	○	○	○	○	○	○	○	○	○	○	○	○	○	○	○	○	○	○	○	○
Thursday	○	○	○	○	○	○	○	○	○	○	○	○	○	○	○	○	○	○	○	○	○	○	○	○
Friday	○	○	○	○	○	○	○	○	○	○	○	○	○	○	○	○	○	○	○	○	○	○	○	○
Saturday	○	○	○	○	○	○	○	○	○	○	○	○	○	○	○	○	○	○	○	○	○	○	○	○
Sunday	○	○	○	○	○	○	○	○	○	○	○	○	○	○	○	○	○	○	○	○	○	○	○	○

Mood

MON
TUE
WED
THU
FRI
SAT
SUN

Daily Water Log

MON	◊ ◊ ◊ ◊ ◊ ◊ ◊ ◊
TUES	◊ ◊ ◊ ◊ ◊ ◊ ◊ ◊
WED	◊ ◊ ◊ ◊ ◊ ◊ ◊ ◊
THU	◊ ◊ ◊ ◊ ◊ ◊ ◊ ◊
FRI	◊ ◊ ◊ ◊ ◊ ◊ ◊ ◊
SAT	◊ ◊ ◊ ◊ ◊ ◊ ◊ ◊
SUN	◊ ◊ ◊ ◊ ◊ ◊ ◊ ◊

Weekly Tally & Notes

Body Measurements:

BUST _____
UPPER ARM _____
WAIST _____
HIPS _____
UPPER LEG _____

Weekly Weight Tracker

CURRENT WEIGHT _____
GOAL WEIGHT _____

bust _____
upper arm _____
waist _____
hips _____
upper leg _____

STRUGGLES

VICTORIES

Notes:

Don't decrease the goal, increase the effort.

Daily Fasting Tracker

	1AM	2AM	3AM	4AM	5AM	6AM	7AM	8AM	9AM	10AM	11AM	12PM	1PM	2PM	3PM	4PM	5PM	6PM	7PM	8PM	9PM	10PM	11PM	12AM
Monday	○	○	○	○	○	○	○	○	○	○	○	○	○	○	○	○	○	○	○	○	○	○	○	○
Tuesday	○	○	○	○	○	○	○	○	○	○	○	○	○	○	○	○	○	○	○	○	○	○	○	○
Wednesday	○	○	○	○	○	○	○	○	○	○	○	○	○	○	○	○	○	○	○	○	○	○	○	○
Thursday	○	○	○	○	○	○	○	○	○	○	○	○	○	○	○	○	○	○	○	○	○	○	○	○
Friday	○	○	○	○	○	○	○	○	○	○	○	○	○	○	○	○	○	○	○	○	○	○	○	○
Saturday	○	○	○	○	○	○	○	○	○	○	○	○	○	○	○	○	○	○	○	○	○	○	○	○
Sunday	○	○	○	○	○	○	○	○	○	○	○	○	○	○	○	○	○	○	○	○	○	○	○	○

Mood

MON
TUE
WED
THU
FRI
SAT
SUN

Daily Water Log

MON	◊ ◊ ◊ ◊ ◊ ◊ ◊ ◊
TUES	◊ ◊ ◊ ◊ ◊ ◊ ◊ ◊
WED	◊ ◊ ◊ ◊ ◊ ◊ ◊ ◊
THU	◊ ◊ ◊ ◊ ◊ ◊ ◊ ◊
FRI	◊ ◊ ◊ ◊ ◊ ◊ ◊ ◊
SAT	◊ ◊ ◊ ◊ ◊ ◊ ◊ ◊
SUN	◊ ◊ ◊ ◊ ◊ ◊ ◊ ◊

Weekly Tally & Notes

Body Measurements:

BUST _____
UPPER ARM _____
WAIST _____
HIPS _____
UPPER LEG _____

Weekly Weight Tracker

CURRENT WEIGHT _____
GOAL WEIGHT _____

STRUGGLES

VICTORIES

Notes:

bust

upper arm

waist

hips

upper leg

If not now... Then when?

Daily Fasting Tracker

	1AM	2AM	3AM	4AM	5AM	6AM	7AM	8AM	9AM	10AM	11AM	12PM	1PM	2PM	3PM	4PM	5PM	6PM	7PM	8PM	9PM	10PM	11PM	12AM
Monday	○	○	○	○	○	○	○	○	○	○	○	○	○	○	○	○	○	○	○	○	○	○	○	○
Tuesday	○	○	○	○	○	○	○	○	○	○	○	○	○	○	○	○	○	○	○	○	○	○	○	○
Wednesday	○	○	○	○	○	○	○	○	○	○	○	○	○	○	○	○	○	○	○	○	○	○	○	○
Thursday	○	○	○	○	○	○	○	○	○	○	○	○	○	○	○	○	○	○	○	○	○	○	○	○
Friday	○	○	○	○	○	○	○	○	○	○	○	○	○	○	○	○	○	○	○	○	○	○	○	○
Saturday	○	○	○	○	○	○	○	○	○	○	○	○	○	○	○	○	○	○	○	○	○	○	○	○
Sunday	○	○	○	○	○	○	○	○	○	○	○	○	○	○	○	○	○	○	○	○	○	○	○	○

Mood

MON
TUE
WED
THU
FRI
SAT
SUN

Daily Water Log

MON	〇 〇 〇 〇 〇 〇 〇 〇
TUES	〇 〇 〇 〇 〇 〇 〇 〇
WED	〇 〇 〇 〇 〇 〇 〇 〇
THU	〇 〇 〇 〇 〇 〇 〇 〇
FRI	〇 〇 〇 〇 〇 〇 〇 〇
SAT	〇 〇 〇 〇 〇 〇 〇 〇
SUN	〇 〇 〇 〇 〇 〇 〇 〇

Weekly Tally & Notes

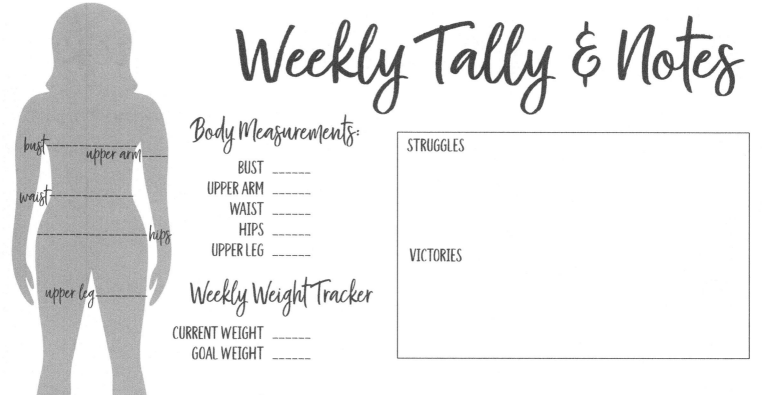

Body Measurements:

BUST _____
UPPER ARM _____
WAIST _____
HIPS _____
UPPER LEG _____

Weekly Weight Tracker

CURRENT WEIGHT _____
GOAL WEIGHT _____

STRUGGLES

VICTORIES

Notes:

It always seems impossible until it's done.

Daily Fasting Tracker

	1AM	2AM	3AM	4AM	5AM	6AM	7AM	8AM	9AM	10AM	11AM	12PM	1PM	2PM	3PM	4PM	5PM	6PM	7PM	8PM	9PM	10PM	11PM	12AM
Monday	○	○	○	○	○	○	○	○	○	○	○	○	○	○	○	○	○	○	○	○	○	○	○	○
Tuesday	○	○	○	○	○	○	○	○	○	○	○	○	○	○	○	○	○	○	○	○	○	○	○	○
Wednesday	○	○	○	○	○	○	○	○	○	○	○	○	○	○	○	○	○	○	○	○	○	○	○	○
Thursday	○	○	○	○	○	○	○	○	○	○	○	○	○	○	○	○	○	○	○	○	○	○	○	○
Friday	○	○	○	○	○	○	○	○	○	○	○	○	○	○	○	○	○	○	○	○	○	○	○	○
Saturday	○	○	○	○	○	○	○	○	○	○	○	○	○	○	○	○	○	○	○	○	○	○	○	○
Sunday	○	○	○	○	○	○	○	○	○	○	○	○	○	○	○	○	○	○	○	○	○	○	○	○

Mood

MON
TUE
WED
THU
FRI
SAT
SUN

Daily Water Log

MON	💧 💧 💧 💧 💧 💧 💧 💧
TUES	💧 💧 💧 💧 💧 💧 💧 💧
WED	💧 💧 💧 💧 💧 💧 💧 💧
THU	💧 💧 💧 💧 💧 💧 💧 💧
FRI	💧 💧 💧 💧 💧 💧 💧 💧
SAT	💧 💧 💧 💧 💧 💧 💧 💧
SUN	💧 💧 💧 💧 💧 💧 💧 💧

Weekly Tally & Notes

Body Measurements:

BUST _____
UPPER ARM _____
WAIST _____
HIPS _____
UPPER LEG _____

Weekly Weight Tracker

CURRENT WEIGHT _____
GOAL WEIGHT _____

bust
upper arm
waist
hips
upper leg

STRUGGLES

VICTORIES

Notes:

Your goals don't care how you feel.

Daily Fasting Tracker

	1AM	2AM	3AM	4AM	5AM	6AM	7AM	8AM	9AM	10AM	11AM	12PM	1PM	2PM	3PM	4PM	5PM	6PM	7PM	8PM	9PM	10PM	11PM	12AM
Monday	○	○	○	○	○	○	○	○	○	○	○	○	○	○	○	○	○	○	○	○	○	○	○	○
Tuesday	○	○	○	○	○	○	○	○	○	○	○	○	○	○	○	○	○	○	○	○	○	○	○	○
Wednesday	○	○	○	○	○	○	○	○	○	○	○	○	○	○	○	○	○	○	○	○	○	○	○	○
Thursday	○	○	○	○	○	○	○	○	○	○	○	○	○	○	○	○	○	○	○	○	○	○	○	○
Friday	○	○	○	○	○	○	○	○	○	○	○	○	○	○	○	○	○	○	○	○	○	○	○	○
Saturday	○	○	○	○	○	○	○	○	○	○	○	○	○	○	○	○	○	○	○	○	○	○	○	○
Sunday	○	○	○	○	○	○	○	○	○	○	○	○	○	○	○	○	○	○	○	○	○	○	○	○

Mood

MON
TUE
WED
THU
FRI
SAT
SUN

Daily Water Log

MON	💧 💧 💧 💧 💧 💧 💧 💧
TUES	💧 💧 💧 💧 💧 💧 💧 💧
WED	💧 💧 💧 💧 💧 💧 💧 💧
THU	💧 💧 💧 💧 💧 💧 💧 💧
FRI	💧 💧 💧 💧 💧 💧 💧 💧
SAT	💧 💧 💧 💧 💧 💧 💧 💧
SUN	💧 💧 💧 💧 💧 💧 💧 💧

Weekly Tally & Notes

Body Measurements:

BUST _____
UPPER ARM _____
WAIST _____
HIPS _____
UPPER LEG _____

Weekly Weight Tracker

CURRENT WEIGHT _____
GOAL WEIGHT _____

bust
upper arm
waist
hips
upper leg

STRUGGLES

VICTORIES

Notes:

Success is an inside job.

Daily Fasting Tracker

	1AM	2AM	3AM	4AM	5AM	6AM	7AM	8AM	9AM	10AM	11AM	12PM	1PM	2PM	3PM	4PM	5PM	6PM	7PM	8PM	9PM	10PM	11PM	12AM
Monday	○	○	○	○	○	○	○	○	○	○	○	○	○	○	○	○	○	○	○	○	○	○	○	○
Tuesday	○	○	○	○	○	○	○	○	○	○	○	○	○	○	○	○	○	○	○	○	○	○	○	○
Wednesday	○	○	○	○	○	○	○	○	○	○	○	○	○	○	○	○	○	○	○	○	○	○	○	○
Thursday	○	○	○	○	○	○	○	○	○	○	○	○	○	○	○	○	○	○	○	○	○	○	○	○
Friday	○	○	○	○	○	○	○	○	○	○	○	○	○	○	○	○	○	○	○	○	○	○	○	○
Saturday	○	○	○	○	○	○	○	○	○	○	○	○	○	○	○	○	○	○	○	○	○	○	○	○
Sunday	○	○	○	○	○	○	○	○	○	○	○	○	○	○	○	○	○	○	○	○	○	○	○	○

Mood

MON
TUE
WED
THU
FRI
SAT
SUN

Daily Water Log

MON	⬦ ⬦ ⬦ ⬦ ⬦ ⬦ ⬦ ⬦
TUES	⬦ ⬦ ⬦ ⬦ ⬦ ⬦ ⬦ ⬦
WED	⬦ ⬦ ⬦ ⬦ ⬦ ⬦ ⬦ ⬦
THU	⬦ ⬦ ⬦ ⬦ ⬦ ⬦ ⬦ ⬦
FRI	⬦ ⬦ ⬦ ⬦ ⬦ ⬦ ⬦ ⬦
SAT	⬦ ⬦ ⬦ ⬦ ⬦ ⬦ ⬦ ⬦
SUN	⬦ ⬦ ⬦ ⬦ ⬦ ⬦ ⬦ ⬦

Weekly Tally & Notes

Body Measurements:

BUST	_____
UPPER ARM	_____
WAIST	_____
HIPS	_____
UPPER LEG	_____

Body silhouette labels: bust, upper arm, waist, hips, upper leg

Weekly Weight Tracker

CURRENT WEIGHT	_____
GOAL WEIGHT	_____

STRUGGLES

VICTORIES

Notes:

Find a way, not an excuse.

Daily Fasting Tracker

	1AM	2AM	3AM	4AM	5AM	6AM	7AM	8AM	9AM	10AM	11AM	12PM	1PM	2PM	3PM	4PM	5PM	6PM	7PM	8PM	9PM	10PM	11PM	12AM
Monday	○	○	○	○	○	○	○	○	○	○	○	○	○	○	○	○	○	○	○	○	○	○	○	○
Tuesday	○	○	○	○	○	○	○	○	○	○	○	○	○	○	○	○	○	○	○	○	○	○	○	○
Wednesday	○	○	○	○	○	○	○	○	○	○	○	○	○	○	○	○	○	○	○	○	○	○	○	○
Thursday	○	○	○	○	○	○	○	○	○	○	○	○	○	○	○	○	○	○	○	○	○	○	○	○
Friday	○	○	○	○	○	○	○	○	○	○	○	○	○	○	○	○	○	○	○	○	○	○	○	○
Saturday	○	○	○	○	○	○	○	○	○	○	○	○	○	○	○	○	○	○	○	○	○	○	○	○
Sunday	○	○	○	○	○	○	○	○	○	○	○	○	○	○	○	○	○	○	○	○	○	○	○	○

Mood

MON
TUE
WED
THU
FRI
SAT
SUN

Daily Water Log

MON	○ ○ ○ ○ ○ ○ ○ ○
TUES	○ ○ ○ ○ ○ ○ ○ ○
WED	○ ○ ○ ○ ○ ○ ○ ○
THU	○ ○ ○ ○ ○ ○ ○ ○
FRI	○ ○ ○ ○ ○ ○ ○ ○
SAT	○ ○ ○ ○ ○ ○ ○ ○
SUN	○ ○ ○ ○ ○ ○ ○ ○

Weekly Tally & Notes

Body Measurements:

BUST _____
UPPER ARM _____
WAIST _____
HIPS _____
UPPER LEG _____

Weekly Weight Tracker

CURRENT WEIGHT _____
GOAL WEIGHT _____

Notes:

STRUGGLES

VICTORIES

bust ———— upper arm ————

waist ————

———— hips

upper leg ————

Be the change you want to see.

Daily Fasting Tracker

	1AM	2AM	3AM	4AM	5AM	6AM	7AM	8AM	9AM	10AM	11AM	12PM	1PM	2PM	3PM	4PM	5PM	6PM	7PM	8PM	9PM	10PM	11PM	12AM
Monday	○	○	○	○	○	○	○	○	○	○	○	○	○	○	○	○	○	○	○	○	○	○	○	○
Tuesday	○	○	○	○	○	○	○	○	○	○	○	○	○	○	○	○	○	○	○	○	○	○	○	○
Wednesday	○	○	○	○	○	○	○	○	○	○	○	○	○	○	○	○	○	○	○	○	○	○	○	○
Thursday	○	○	○	○	○	○	○	○	○	○	○	○	○	○	○	○	○	○	○	○	○	○	○	○
Friday	○	○	○	○	○	○	○	○	○	○	○	○	○	○	○	○	○	○	○	○	○	○	○	○
Saturday	○	○	○	○	○	○	○	○	○	○	○	○	○	○	○	○	○	○	○	○	○	○	○	○
Sunday	○	○	○	○	○	○	○	○	○	○	○	○	○	○	○	○	○	○	○	○	○	○	○	○

Mood

MON

TUE

WED

THU

FRI

SAT

SUN

Daily Water Log

MON

TUES

WED

THU

FRI

SAT

SUN

Weekly Tally & Notes

Body Measurements:

BUST _____
UPPER ARM _____
WAIST _____
HIPS _____
UPPER LEG _____

Weekly Weight Tracker

CURRENT WEIGHT _____
GOAL WEIGHT _____

bust _____
upper arm _____
waist _____
hips _____
upper leg _____

STRUGGLES

VICTORIES

Notes:

Work hard and make it happen.

Daily Fasting Tracker

	1AM	2AM	3AM	4AM	5AM	6AM	7AM	8AM	9AM	10AM	11AM	12PM	1PM	2PM	3PM	4PM	5PM	6PM	7PM	8PM	9PM	10PM	11PM	12AM
Monday	○	○	○	○	○	○	○	○	○	○	○	○	○	○	○	○	○	○	○	○	○	○	○	○
Tuesday	○	○	○	○	○	○	○	○	○	○	○	○	○	○	○	○	○	○	○	○	○	○	○	○
Wednesday	○	○	○	○	○	○	○	○	○	○	○	○	○	○	○	○	○	○	○	○	○	○	○	○
Thursday	○	○	○	○	○	○	○	○	○	○	○	○	○	○	○	○	○	○	○	○	○	○	○	○
Friday	○	○	○	○	○	○	○	○	○	○	○	○	○	○	○	○	○	○	○	○	○	○	○	○
Saturday	○	○	○	○	○	○	○	○	○	○	○	○	○	○	○	○	○	○	○	○	○	○	○	○
Sunday	○	○	○	○	○	○	○	○	○	○	○	○	○	○	○	○	○	○	○	○	○	○	○	○

Mood

MON
TUE
WED
THU
FRI
SAT
SUN

Daily Water Log

MON	○ ○ ○ ○ ○ ○ ○ ○
TUES	○ ○ ○ ○ ○ ○ ○ ○
WED	○ ○ ○ ○ ○ ○ ○ ○
THU	○ ○ ○ ○ ○ ○ ○ ○
FRI	○ ○ ○ ○ ○ ○ ○ ○
SAT	○ ○ ○ ○ ○ ○ ○ ○
SUN	○ ○ ○ ○ ○ ○ ○ ○

Weekly Tally & Notes

Body Measurements:

BUST _____
UPPER ARM _____
WAIST _____
HIPS _____
UPPER LEG _____

Weekly Weight Tracker

CURRENT WEIGHT _____
GOAL WEIGHT _____

Notes:

bust

upper arm

waist

hips

upper leg

STRUGGLES

VICTORIES

Be the best version of you.

Daily Fasting Tracker

	1AM	2AM	3AM	4AM	5AM	6AM	7AM	8AM	9AM	10AM	11AM	12PM	1PM	2PM	3PM	4PM	5PM	6PM	7PM	8PM	9PM	10PM	11PM	12AM
Monday	○	○	○	○	○	○	○	○	○	○	○	○	○	○	○	○	○	○	○	○	○	○	○	○
Tuesday	○	○	○	○	○	○	○	○	○	○	○	○	○	○	○	○	○	○	○	○	○	○	○	○
Wednesday	○	○	○	○	○	○	○	○	○	○	○	○	○	○	○	○	○	○	○	○	○	○	○	○
Thursday	○	○	○	○	○	○	○	○	○	○	○	○	○	○	○	○	○	○	○	○	○	○	○	○
Friday	○	○	○	○	○	○	○	○	○	○	○	○	○	○	○	○	○	○	○	○	○	○	○	○
Saturday	○	○	○	○	○	○	○	○	○	○	○	○	○	○	○	○	○	○	○	○	○	○	○	○
Sunday	○	○	○	○	○	○	○	○	○	○	○	○	○	○	○	○	○	○	○	○	○	○	○	○

Mood

MON

TUE

WED

THU

FRI

SAT

SUN

Daily Water Log

MON	○ ○ ○ ○ ○ ○ ○ ○
TUES	○ ○ ○ ○ ○ ○ ○ ○
WED	○ ○ ○ ○ ○ ○ ○ ○
THU	○ ○ ○ ○ ○ ○ ○ ○
FRI	○ ○ ○ ○ ○ ○ ○ ○
SAT	○ ○ ○ ○ ○ ○ ○ ○
SUN	○ ○ ○ ○ ○ ○ ○ ○

Weekly Tally & Notes

Body Measurements:

BUST _____
UPPER ARM _____
WAIST _____
HIPS _____
UPPER LEG _____

Weekly Weight Tracker

CURRENT WEIGHT _____
GOAL WEIGHT _____

bust

upper arm

waist

hips

upper leg

STRUGGLES

VICTORIES

Notes:

Your attitude determines your direction.

Daily Fasting Tracker

	1AM	2AM	3AM	4AM	5AM	6AM	7AM	8AM	9AM	10AM	11AM	12PM	1PM	2PM	3PM	4PM	5PM	6PM	7PM	8PM	9PM	10PM	11PM	12AM
Monday	○	○	○	○	○	○	○	○	○	○	○	○	○	○	○	○	○	○	○	○	○	○	○	○
Tuesday	○	○	○	○	○	○	○	○	○	○	○	○	○	○	○	○	○	○	○	○	○	○	○	○
Wednesday	○	○	○	○	○	○	○	○	○	○	○	○	○	○	○	○	○	○	○	○	○	○	○	○
Thursday	○	○	○	○	○	○	○	○	○	○	○	○	○	○	○	○	○	○	○	○	○	○	○	○
Friday	○	○	○	○	○	○	○	○	○	○	○	○	○	○	○	○	○	○	○	○	○	○	○	○
Saturday	○	○	○	○	○	○	○	○	○	○	○	○	○	○	○	○	○	○	○	○	○	○	○	○
Sunday	○	○	○	○	○	○	○	○	○	○	○	○	○	○	○	○	○	○	○	○	○	○	○	○

Mood

MON
TUE
WED
THU
FRI
SAT
SUN

Daily Water Log

MON
TUES
WED
THU
FRI
SAT
SUN

Weekly Tally & Notes

bust – – – – – – – – – –
upper arm – – – – – –
waist – – – – – – – – – –
hips – – – – – – –
upper leg – – – – – –

Body Measurements:

BUST _ _ _ _ _ _
UPPER ARM _ _ _ _ _ _
WAIST _ _ _ _ _ _
HIPS _ _ _ _ _ _
UPPER LEG _ _ _ _ _ _

Weekly Weight Tracker

CURRENT WEIGHT _ _ _ _ _ _
GOAL WEIGHT _ _ _ _ _ _

STRUGGLES

VICTORIES

Notes:

Amazing things happen when you try.

Daily Fasting Tracker

	1AM	2AM	3AM	4AM	5AM	6AM	7AM	8AM	9AM	10AM	11AM	12PM	1PM	2PM	3PM	4PM	5PM	6PM	7PM	8PM	9PM	10PM	11PM	12AM
Monday	○	○	○	○	○	○	○	○	○	○	○	○	○	○	○	○	○	○	○	○	○	○	○	○
Tuesday	○	○	○	○	○	○	○	○	○	○	○	○	○	○	○	○	○	○	○	○	○	○	○	○
Wednesday	○	○	○	○	○	○	○	○	○	○	○	○	○	○	○	○	○	○	○	○	○	○	○	○
Thursday	○	○	○	○	○	○	○	○	○	○	○	○	○	○	○	○	○	○	○	○	○	○	○	○
Friday	○	○	○	○	○	○	○	○	○	○	○	○	○	○	○	○	○	○	○	○	○	○	○	○
Saturday	○	○	○	○	○	○	○	○	○	○	○	○	○	○	○	○	○	○	○	○	○	○	○	○
Sunday	○	○	○	○	○	○	○	○	○	○	○	○	○	○	○	○	○	○	○	○	○	○	○	○

Mood

MON

TUE

WED

THU

FRI

SAT

SUN

Daily Water Log

MON

TUES

WED

THU

FRI

SAT

SUN

Weekly Tally & Notes

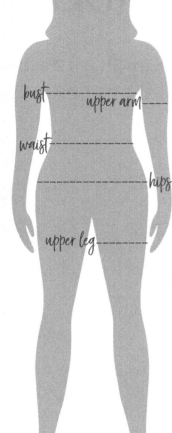

Body Measurements:

BUST _____
UPPER ARM _____
WAIST _____
HIPS _____
UPPER LEG _____

Weekly Weight Tracker

CURRENT WEIGHT _____
GOAL WEIGHT _____

Notes:

STRUGGLES

VICTORIES

The only way you see results is if you stay consistent.

Daily Fasting Tracker

	1AM	2AM	3AM	4AM	5AM	6AM	7AM	8AM	9AM	10AM	11AM	12PM	1PM	2PM	3PM	4PM	5PM	6PM	7PM	8PM	9PM	10PM	11PM	12AM
Monday	○	○	○	○	○	○	○	○	○	○	○	○	○	○	○	○	○	○	○	○	○	○	○	○
Tuesday	○	○	○	○	○	○	○	○	○	○	○	○	○	○	○	○	○	○	○	○	○	○	○	○
Wednesday	○	○	○	○	○	○	○	○	○	○	○	○	○	○	○	○	○	○	○	○	○	○	○	○
Thursday	○	○	○	○	○	○	○	○	○	○	○	○	○	○	○	○	○	○	○	○	○	○	○	○
Friday	○	○	○	○	○	○	○	○	○	○	○	○	○	○	○	○	○	○	○	○	○	○	○	○
Saturday	○	○	○	○	○	○	○	○	○	○	○	○	○	○	○	○	○	○	○	○	○	○	○	○
Sunday	○	○	○	○	○	○	○	○	○	○	○	○	○	○	○	○	○	○	○	○	○	○	○	○

Mood

Daily Water Log

MON	◊ ◊ ◊ ◊ ◊ ◊ ◊ ◊
TUES	◊ ◊ ◊ ◊ ◊ ◊ ◊ ◊
WED	◊ ◊ ◊ ◊ ◊ ◊ ◊ ◊
THU	◊ ◊ ◊ ◊ ◊ ◊ ◊ ◊
FRI	◊ ◊ ◊ ◊ ◊ ◊ ◊ ◊
SAT	◊ ◊ ◊ ◊ ◊ ◊ ◊ ◊
SUN	◊ ◊ ◊ ◊ ◊ ◊ ◊ ◊

Weekly Tally & Notes

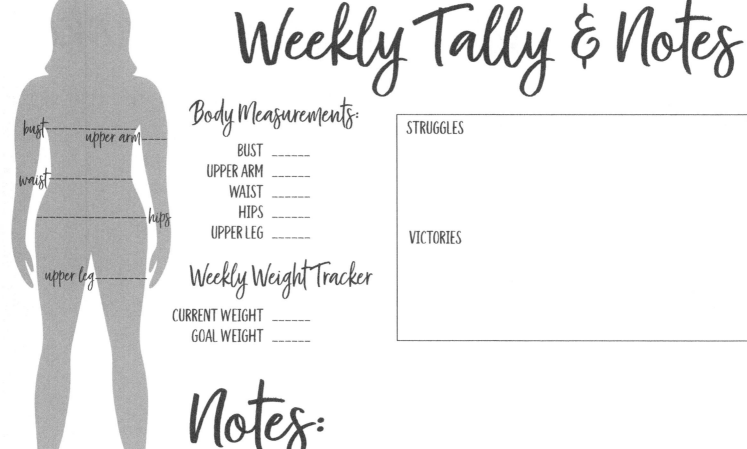

Body Measurements:

BUST _____

UPPER ARM _____

WAIST _____

HIPS _____

UPPER LEG _____

Weekly Weight Tracker

CURRENT WEIGHT _____

GOAL WEIGHT _____

STRUGGLES

VICTORIES

Notes:

Flowers need time to bloom, so do you.

Daily Fasting Tracker

	1AM	2AM	3AM	4AM	5AM	6AM	7AM	8AM	9AM	10AM	11AM	12PM	1PM	2PM	3PM	4PM	5PM	6PM	7PM	8PM	9PM	10PM	11PM	12AM
Monday	○	○	○	○	○	○	○	○	○	○	○	○	○	○	○	○	○	○	○	○	○	○	○	○
Tuesday	○	○	○	○	○	○	○	○	○	○	○	○	○	○	○	○	○	○	○	○	○	○	○	○
Wednesday	○	○	○	○	○	○	○	○	○	○	○	○	○	○	○	○	○	○	○	○	○	○	○	○
Thursday	○	○	○	○	○	○	○	○	○	○	○	○	○	○	○	○	○	○	○	○	○	○	○	○
Friday	○	○	○	○	○	○	○	○	○	○	○	○	○	○	○	○	○	○	○	○	○	○	○	○
Saturday	○	○	○	○	○	○	○	○	○	○	○	○	○	○	○	○	○	○	○	○	○	○	○	○
Sunday	○	○	○	○	○	○	○	○	○	○	○	○	○	○	○	○	○	○	○	○	○	○	○	○

Mood

MON

TUE

WED

THU

FRI

SAT

SUN

Daily Water Log

MON 🖤🖤🖤🖤🖤🖤🖤🖤

TUES 🖤🖤🖤🖤🖤🖤🖤🖤

WED 🖤🖤🖤🖤🖤🖤🖤🖤

THU 🖤🖤🖤🖤🖤🖤🖤🖤

FRI 🖤🖤🖤🖤🖤🖤🖤🖤

SAT 🖤🖤🖤🖤🖤🖤🖤🖤

SUN 🖤🖤🖤🖤🖤🖤🖤🖤

Weekly Tally & Notes

Body Measurements:

BUST _____
UPPER ARM _____
WAIST _____
HIPS _____
UPPER LEG _____

Weekly Weight Tracker

CURRENT WEIGHT _____
GOAL WEIGHT _____

bust _____
upper arm _____
waist _____
hips _____
upper leg _____

STRUGGLES

VICTORIES

Notes:

Trust the process.

Daily Fasting Tracker

	1AM	2AM	3AM	4AM	5AM	6AM	7AM	8AM	9AM	10AM	11AM	12PM	1PM	2PM	3PM	4PM	5PM	6PM	7PM	8PM	9PM	10PM	11PM	12AM
Monday	○	○	○	○	○	○	○	○	○	○	○	○	○	○	○	○	○	○	○	○	○	○	○	○
Tuesday	○	○	○	○	○	○	○	○	○	○	○	○	○	○	○	○	○	○	○	○	○	○	○	○
Wednesday	○	○	○	○	○	○	○	○	○	○	○	○	○	○	○	○	○	○	○	○	○	○	○	○
Thursday	○	○	○	○	○	○	○	○	○	○	○	○	○	○	○	○	○	○	○	○	○	○	○	○
Friday	○	○	○	○	○	○	○	○	○	○	○	○	○	○	○	○	○	○	○	○	○	○	○	○
Saturday	○	○	○	○	○	○	○	○	○	○	○	○	○	○	○	○	○	○	○	○	○	○	○	○
Sunday	○	○	○	○	○	○	○	○	○	○	○	○	○	○	○	○	○	○	○	○	○	○	○	○

Mood

MON
TUE
WED
THU
FRI
SAT
SUN

Daily Water Log

MON	💧 💧 💧 💧 💧 💧 💧 💧
TUES	💧 💧 💧 💧 💧 💧 💧 💧
WED	💧 💧 💧 💧 💧 💧 💧 💧
THU	💧 💧 💧 💧 💧 💧 💧 💧
FRI	💧 💧 💧 💧 💧 💧 💧 💧
SAT	💧 💧 💧 💧 💧 💧 💧 💧
SUN	💧 💧 💧 💧 💧 💧 💧 💧

Weekly Tally & Notes

bust

upper arm

waist

hips

upper leg

Body Measurements:

BUST _____

UPPER ARM _____

WAIST _____

HIPS _____

UPPER LEG _____

Weekly Weight Tracker

CURRENT WEIGHT _____

GOAL WEIGHT _____

STRUGGLES

VICTORIES

Notes:

Success = 20% strategy + 80% mindset

Daily Fasting Tracker

	1AM	2AM	3AM	4AM	5AM	6AM	7AM	8AM	9AM	10AM	11AM	12PM	1PM	2PM	3PM	4PM	5PM	6PM	7PM	8PM	9PM	10PM	11PM	12AM
Monday	○	○	○	○	○	○	○	○	○	○	○	○	○	○	○	○	○	○	○	○	○	○	○	○
Tuesday	○	○	○	○	○	○	○	○	○	○	○	○	○	○	○	○	○	○	○	○	○	○	○	○
Wednesday	○	○	○	○	○	○	○	○	○	○	○	○	○	○	○	○	○	○	○	○	○	○	○	○
Thursday	○	○	○	○	○	○	○	○	○	○	○	○	○	○	○	○	○	○	○	○	○	○	○	○
Friday	○	○	○	○	○	○	○	○	○	○	○	○	○	○	○	○	○	○	○	○	○	○	○	○
Saturday	○	○	○	○	○	○	○	○	○	○	○	○	○	○	○	○	○	○	○	○	○	○	○	○
Sunday	○	○	○	○	○	○	○	○	○	○	○	○	○	○	○	○	○	○	○	○	○	○	○	○

Mood

MON
TUE
WED
THU
FRI
SAT
SUN

Daily Water Log

MON
TUES
WED
THU
FRI
SAT
SUN

Weekly Tally & Notes

Body Measurements:

BUST _____
UPPER ARM _____
WAIST _____
HIPS _____
UPPER LEG _____

Weekly Weight Tracker

CURRENT WEIGHT _____
GOAL WEIGHT _____

bust
upper arm
waist
hips
upper leg

STRUGGLES

VICTORIES

Notes:

Good things take time.

Daily Fasting Tracker

	1AM	2AM	3AM	4AM	5AM	6AM	7AM	8AM	9AM	10AM	11AM	12PM	1PM	2PM	3PM	4PM	5PM	6PM	7PM	8PM	9PM	10PM	11PM	12AM
Monday	○	○	○	○	○	○	○	○	○	○	○	○	○	○	○	○	○	○	○	○	○	○	○	○
Tuesday	○	○	○	○	○	○	○	○	○	○	○	○	○	○	○	○	○	○	○	○	○	○	○	○
Wednesday	○	○	○	○	○	○	○	○	○	○	○	○	○	○	○	○	○	○	○	○	○	○	○	○
Thursday	○	○	○	○	○	○	○	○	○	○	○	○	○	○	○	○	○	○	○	○	○	○	○	○
Friday	○	○	○	○	○	○	○	○	○	○	○	○	○	○	○	○	○	○	○	○	○	○	○	○
Saturday	○	○	○	○	○	○	○	○	○	○	○	○	○	○	○	○	○	○	○	○	○	○	○	○
Sunday	○	○	○	○	○	○	○	○	○	○	○	○	○	○	○	○	○	○	○	○	○	○	○	○

Mood

MON

TUE

WED

THU

FRI

SAT

SUN

Daily Water Log

MON	〇 〇 〇 〇 〇 〇 〇 〇
TUES	〇 〇 〇 〇 〇 〇 〇 〇
WED	〇 〇 〇 〇 〇 〇 〇 〇
THU	〇 〇 〇 〇 〇 〇 〇 〇
FRI	〇 〇 〇 〇 〇 〇 〇 〇
SAT	〇 〇 〇 〇 〇 〇 〇 〇
SUN	〇 〇 〇 〇 〇 〇 〇 〇

Weekly Tally & Notes

Body Measurements:

BUST _____
UPPER ARM _____
WAIST _____
HIPS _____
UPPER LEG _____

Weekly Weight Tracker

CURRENT WEIGHT _____
GOAL WEIGHT _____

bust
upper arm
waist
hips
upper leg

STRUGGLES

VICTORIES

Notes:

Make yourself a priority.

Daily Fasting Tracker

	1AM	2AM	3AM	4AM	5AM	6AM	7AM	8AM	9AM	10AM	11AM	12PM	1PM	2PM	3PM	4PM	5PM	6PM	7PM	8PM	9PM	10PM	11PM	12AM
Monday	○	○	○	○	○	○	○	○	○	○	○	○	○	○	○	○	○	○	○	○	○	○	○	○
Tuesday	○	○	○	○	○	○	○	○	○	○	○	○	○	○	○	○	○	○	○	○	○	○	○	○
Wednesday	○	○	○	○	○	○	○	○	○	○	○	○	○	○	○	○	○	○	○	○	○	○	○	○
Thursday	○	○	○	○	○	○	○	○	○	○	○	○	○	○	○	○	○	○	○	○	○	○	○	○
Friday	○	○	○	○	○	○	○	○	○	○	○	○	○	○	○	○	○	○	○	○	○	○	○	○
Saturday	○	○	○	○	○	○	○	○	○	○	○	○	○	○	○	○	○	○	○	○	○	○	○	○
Sunday	○	○	○	○	○	○	○	○	○	○	○	○	○	○	○	○	○	○	○	○	○	○	○	○

Mood

MON

TUE

WED

THU

FRI

SAT

SUN

Daily Water Log

MON	◇ ◇ ◇ ◇ ◇ ◇ ◇ ◇
TUES	◇ ◇ ◇ ◇ ◇ ◇ ◇ ◇
WED	◇ ◇ ◇ ◇ ◇ ◇ ◇ ◇
THU	◇ ◇ ◇ ◇ ◇ ◇ ◇ ◇
FRI	◇ ◇ ◇ ◇ ◇ ◇ ◇ ◇
SAT	◇ ◇ ◇ ◇ ◇ ◇ ◇ ◇
SUN	◇ ◇ ◇ ◇ ◇ ◇ ◇ ◇

Weekly Tally & Notes

Body Measurements:

BUST _____
UPPER ARM _____
WAIST _____
HIPS _____
UPPER LEG _____

Weekly Weight Tracker

CURRENT WEIGHT _____
GOAL WEIGHT _____

bust _____
upper arm _____
waist _____
hips _____
upper leg _____

STRUGGLES

VICTORIES

Notes:

If you want it, work for it.

Daily Fasting Tracker

	1AM	2AM	3AM	4AM	5AM	6AM	7AM	8AM	9AM	10AM	11AM	12PM	1PM	2PM	3PM	4PM	5PM	6PM	7PM	8PM	9PM	10PM	11PM	12AM
Monday	○	○	○	○	○	○	○	○	○	○	○	○	○	○	○	○	○	○	○	○	○	○	○	○
Tuesday	○	○	○	○	○	○	○	○	○	○	○	○	○	○	○	○	○	○	○	○	○	○	○	○
Wednesday	○	○	○	○	○	○	○	○	○	○	○	○	○	○	○	○	○	○	○	○	○	○	○	○
Thursday	○	○	○	○	○	○	○	○	○	○	○	○	○	○	○	○	○	○	○	○	○	○	○	○
Friday	○	○	○	○	○	○	○	○	○	○	○	○	○	○	○	○	○	○	○	○	○	○	○	○
Saturday	○	○	○	○	○	○	○	○	○	○	○	○	○	○	○	○	○	○	○	○	○	○	○	○
Sunday	○	○	○	○	○	○	○	○	○	○	○	○	○	○	○	○	○	○	○	○	○	○	○	○

Mood

MON
TUE
WED
THU
FRI
SAT
SUN

Daily Water Log

MON	◇ ◇ ◇ ◇ ◇ ◇ ◇ ◇
TUES	◇ ◇ ◇ ◇ ◇ ◇ ◇ ◇
WED	◇ ◇ ◇ ◇ ◇ ◇ ◇ ◇
THU	◇ ◇ ◇ ◇ ◇ ◇ ◇ ◇
FRI	◇ ◇ ◇ ◇ ◇ ◇ ◇ ◇
SAT	◇ ◇ ◇ ◇ ◇ ◇ ◇ ◇
SUN	◇ ◇ ◇ ◇ ◇ ◇ ◇

Weekly Tally & Notes

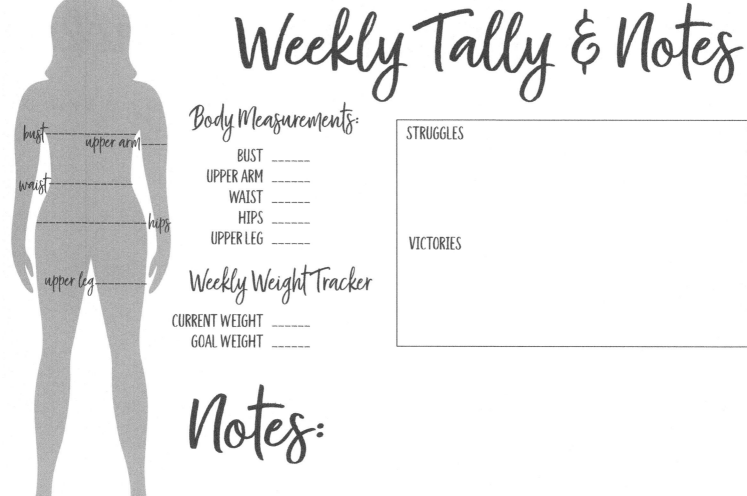

Body Measurements:

BUST _____
UPPER ARM _____
WAIST _____
HIPS _____
UPPER LEG _____

Weekly Weight Tracker

CURRENT WEIGHT _____
GOAL WEIGHT _____

Notes:

STRUGGLES

VICTORIES

There is no change where there is no action.

Daily Fasting Tracker

	1AM	2AM	3AM	4AM	5AM	6AM	7AM	8AM	9AM	10AM	11AM	12PM	1PM	2PM	3PM	4PM	5PM	6PM	7PM	8PM	9PM	10PM	11PM	12AM
Monday	○	○	○	○	○	○	○	○	○	○	○	○	○	○	○	○	○	○	○	○	○	○	○	○
Tuesday	○	○	○	○	○	○	○	○	○	○	○	○	○	○	○	○	○	○	○	○	○	○	○	○
Wednesday	○	○	○	○	○	○	○	○	○	○	○	○	○	○	○	○	○	○	○	○	○	○	○	○
Thursday	○	○	○	○	○	○	○	○	○	○	○	○	○	○	○	○	○	○	○	○	○	○	○	○
Friday	○	○	○	○	○	○	○	○	○	○	○	○	○	○	○	○	○	○	○	○	○	○	○	○
Saturday	○	○	○	○	○	○	○	○	○	○	○	○	○	○	○	○	○	○	○	○	○	○	○	○
Sunday	○	○	○	○	○	○	○	○	○	○	○	○	○	○	○	○	○	○	○	○	○	○	○	○

Mood

MON
TUE
WED
THU
FRI
SAT
SUN

Daily Water Log

MON
TUES
WED
THU
FRI
SAT
SUN

Weekly Tally & Notes

Body Measurements:

BUST _____
UPPER ARM _____
WAIST _____
HIPS _____
UPPER LEG _____

Weekly Weight Tracker

CURRENT WEIGHT _____
GOAL WEIGHT _____

Notes:

bust
upper arm
waist
hips
upper leg

STRUGGLES

VICTORIES

Decide. Commit. Succeed.

Daily Fasting Tracker

	1AM	2AM	3AM	4AM	5AM	6AM	7AM	8AM	9AM	10AM	11AM	12PM	1PM	2PM	3PM	4PM	5PM	6PM	7PM	8PM	9PM	10PM	11PM	12AM
Monday	○	○	○	○	○	○	○	○	○	○	○	○	○	○	○	○	○	○	○	○	○	○	○	○
Tuesday	○	○	○	○	○	○	○	○	○	○	○	○	○	○	○	○	○	○	○	○	○	○	○	○
Wednesday	○	○	○	○	○	○	○	○	○	○	○	○	○	○	○	○	○	○	○	○	○	○	○	○
Thursday	○	○	○	○	○	○	○	○	○	○	○	○	○	○	○	○	○	○	○	○	○	○	○	○
Friday	○	○	○	○	○	○	○	○	○	○	○	○	○	○	○	○	○	○	○	○	○	○	○	○
Saturday	○	○	○	○	○	○	○	○	○	○	○	○	○	○	○	○	○	○	○	○	○	○	○	○
Sunday	○	○	○	○	○	○	○	○	○	○	○	○	○	○	○	○	○	○	○	○	○	○	○	○

Mood

MON
TUE
WED
THU
FRI
SAT
SUN

Daily Water Log

MON	◊ ◊ ◊ ◊ ◊ ◊ ◊ ◊
TUES	◊ ◊ ◊ ◊ ◊ ◊ ◊ ◊
WED	◊ ◊ ◊ ◊ ◊ ◊ ◊ ◊
THU	◊ ◊ ◊ ◊ ◊ ◊ ◊ ◊
FRI	◊ ◊ ◊ ◊ ◊ ◊ ◊ ◊
SAT	◊ ◊ ◊ ◊ ◊ ◊ ◊ ◊
SUN	◊ ◊ ◊ ◊ ◊ ◊ ◊ ◊

Weekly Tally & Notes

Body Measurements:

bust

upper arm

waist

hips

upper leg

BUST _____
UPPER ARM _____
WAIST _____
HIPS _____
UPPER LEG _____

Weekly Weight Tracker

CURRENT WEIGHT _____
GOAL WEIGHT _____

STRUGGLES

VICTORIES

Notes:

Everyday is a fresh start.

Daily Fasting Tracker

	1AM	2AM	3AM	4AM	5AM	6AM	7AM	8AM	9AM	10AM	11AM	12PM	1PM	2PM	3PM	4PM	5PM	6PM	7PM	8PM	9PM	10PM	11PM	12AM
Monday	○	○	○	○	○	○	○	○	○	○	○	○	○	○	○	○	○	○	○	○	○	○	○	○
Tuesday	○	○	○	○	○	○	○	○	○	○	○	○	○	○	○	○	○	○	○	○	○	○	○	○
Wednesday	○	○	○	○	○	○	○	○	○	○	○	○	○	○	○	○	○	○	○	○	○	○	○	○
Thursday	○	○	○	○	○	○	○	○	○	○	○	○	○	○	○	○	○	○	○	○	○	○	○	○
Friday	○	○	○	○	○	○	○	○	○	○	○	○	○	○	○	○	○	○	○	○	○	○	○	○
Saturday	○	○	○	○	○	○	○	○	○	○	○	○	○	○	○	○	○	○	○	○	○	○	○	○
Sunday	○	○	○	○	○	○	○	○	○	○	○	○	○	○	○	○	○	○	○	○	○	○	○	○

Mood

MON
TUE
WED
THU
FRI
SAT
SUN

Daily Water Log

MON	○ ○ ○ ○ ○ ○ ○ ○
TUES	○ ○ ○ ○ ○ ○ ○
WED	○ ○ ○ ○ ○ ○ ○
THU	○ ○ ○ ○ ○ ○ ○
FRI	○ ○ ○ ○ ○ ○ ○
SAT	○ ○ ○ ○ ○ ○ ○
SUN	○ ○ ○ ○ ○ ○ ○

Weekly Tally & Notes

Body Measurements:

BUST _____
UPPER ARM _____
WAIST _____
HIPS _____
UPPER LEG _____

Weekly Weight Tracker

CURRENT WEIGHT _____
GOAL WEIGHT _____

bust _____
upper arm _____
waist _____
hips _____
upper leg _____

STRUGGLES

VICTORIES

Notes:

Great things never came from comfort zones.

Daily Fasting Tracker

	1AM	2AM	3AM	4AM	5AM	6AM	7AM	8AM	9AM	10AM	11AM	12PM	1PM	2PM	3PM	4PM	5PM	6PM	7PM	8PM	9PM	10PM	11PM	12AM
Monday	○	○	○	○	○	○	○	○	○	○	○	○	○	○	○	○	○	○	○	○	○	○	○	○
Tuesday	○	○	○	○	○	○	○	○	○	○	○	○	○	○	○	○	○	○	○	○	○	○	○	○
Wednesday	○	○	○	○	○	○	○	○	○	○	○	○	○	○	○	○	○	○	○	○	○	○	○	○
Thursday	○	○	○	○	○	○	○	○	○	○	○	○	○	○	○	○	○	○	○	○	○	○	○	○
Friday	○	○	○	○	○	○	○	○	○	○	○	○	○	○	○	○	○	○	○	○	○	○	○	○
Saturday	○	○	○	○	○	○	○	○	○	○	○	○	○	○	○	○	○	○	○	○	○	○	○	○
Sunday	○	○	○	○	○	○	○	○	○	○	○	○	○	○	○	○	○	○	○	○	○	○	○	○

Mood

MON
TUE
WED
THU
FRI
SAT
SUN

Daily Water Log

MON	○ ○ ○ ○ ○ ○ ○ ○
TUES	○ ○ ○ ○ ○ ○ ○
WED	○ ○ ○ ○ ○ ○ ○ ○
THU	○ ○ ○ ○ ○ ○ ○
FRI	○ ○ ○ ○ ○ ○ ○ ○
SAT	○ ○ ○ ○ ○ ○ ○
SUN	○ ○ ○ ○ ○ ○ ○

Weekly Tally & Notes

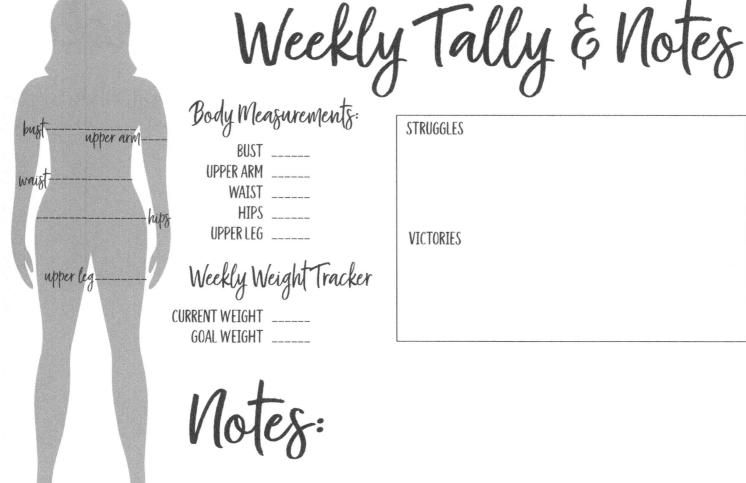

Body Measurements:

BUST	_____
UPPER ARM	_____
WAIST	_____
HIPS	_____
UPPER LEG	_____

Weekly Weight Tracker

CURRENT WEIGHT _____
GOAL WEIGHT _____

STRUGGLES

VICTORIES

Notes:

What you do today can improve all your tomorrows.

Daily Fasting Tracker

	1AM	2AM	3AM	4AM	5AM	6AM	7AM	8AM	9AM	10AM	11AM	12PM	1PM	2PM	3PM	4PM	5PM	6PM	7PM	8PM	9PM	10PM	11PM	12AM
Monday	○	○	○	○	○	○	○	○	○	○	○	○	○	○	○	○	○	○	○	○	○	○	○	○
Tuesday	○	○	○	○	○	○	○	○	○	○	○	○	○	○	○	○	○	○	○	○	○	○	○	○
Wednesday	○	○	○	○	○	○	○	○	○	○	○	○	○	○	○	○	○	○	○	○	○	○	○	○
Thursday	○	○	○	○	○	○	○	○	○	○	○	○	○	○	○	○	○	○	○	○	○	○	○	○
Friday	○	○	○	○	○	○	○	○	○	○	○	○	○	○	○	○	○	○	○	○	○	○	○	○
Saturday	○	○	○	○	○	○	○	○	○	○	○	○	○	○	○	○	○	○	○	○	○	○	○	○
Sunday	○	○	○	○	○	○	○	○	○	○	○	○	○	○	○	○	○	○	○	○	○	○	○	○

Mood

MON
TUE
WED
THU
FRI
SAT
SUN

Daily Water Log

MON	○ ○ ○ ○ ○ ○ ○ ○
TUES	○ ○ ○ ○ ○ ○ ○ ○
WED	○ ○ ○ ○ ○ ○ ○ ○
THU	○ ○ ○ ○ ○ ○ ○ ○
FRI	○ ○ ○ ○ ○ ○ ○ ○
SAT	○ ○ ○ ○ ○ ○ ○ ○
SUN	○ ○ ○ ○ ○ ○ ○ ○

Weekly Tally & Notes

Body Measurements:

BUST _____
UPPER ARM _____
WAIST _____
HIPS _____
UPPER LEG _____

bust ————
upper arm ————
waist ————
hips
upper leg ————

Weekly Weight Tracker

CURRENT WEIGHT _____
GOAL WEIGHT _____

STRUGGLES

VICTORIES

Notes:

Good things come to those who work for it.

Daily Fasting Tracker

	1AM	2AM	3AM	4AM	5AM	6AM	7AM	8AM	9AM	10AM	11AM	12PM	1PM	2PM	3PM	4PM	5PM	6PM	7PM	8PM	9PM	10PM	11PM	12AM
Monday	○	○	○	○	○	○	○	○	○	○	○	○	○	○	○	○	○	○	○	○	○	○	○	○
Tuesday	○	○	○	○	○	○	○	○	○	○	○	○	○	○	○	○	○	○	○	○	○	○	○	○
Wednesday	○	○	○	○	○	○	○	○	○	○	○	○	○	○	○	○	○	○	○	○	○	○	○	○
Thursday	○	○	○	○	○	○	○	○	○	○	○	○	○	○	○	○	○	○	○	○	○	○	○	○
Friday	○	○	○	○	○	○	○	○	○	○	○	○	○	○	○	○	○	○	○	○	○	○	○	○
Saturday	○	○	○	○	○	○	○	○	○	○	○	○	○	○	○	○	○	○	○	○	○	○	○	○
Sunday	○	○	○	○	○	○	○	○	○	○	○	○	○	○	○	○	○	○	○	○	○	○	○	○

Mood

MON
TUE
WED
THU
FRI
SAT
SUN

Daily Water Log

MON
TUES
WED
THU
FRI
SAT
SUN

Weekly Tally & Notes

Body Measurements:

BUST _____
UPPER ARM _____
WAIST _____
HIPS _____
UPPER LEG _____

bust _____
upper arm _____
waist _____
hips _____
upper leg _____

Weekly Weight Tracker

CURRENT WEIGHT _____
GOAL WEIGHT _____

STRUGGLES

VICTORIES

Notes:

You are stronger than you think.

Daily Fasting Tracker

	1AM	2AM	3AM	4AM	5AM	6AM	7AM	8AM	9AM	10AM	11AM	12PM	1PM	2PM	3PM	4PM	5PM	6PM	7PM	8PM	9PM	10PM	11PM	12AM
Monday	○	○	○	○	○	○	○	○	○	○	○	○	○	○	○	○	○	○	○	○	○	○	○	○
Tuesday	○	○	○	○	○	○	○	○	○	○	○	○	○	○	○	○	○	○	○	○	○	○	○	○
Wednesday	○	○	○	○	○	○	○	○	○	○	○	○	○	○	○	○	○	○	○	○	○	○	○	○
Thursday	○	○	○	○	○	○	○	○	○	○	○	○	○	○	○	○	○	○	○	○	○	○	○	○
Friday	○	○	○	○	○	○	○	○	○	○	○	○	○	○	○	○	○	○	○	○	○	○	○	○
Saturday	○	○	○	○	○	○	○	○	○	○	○	○	○	○	○	○	○	○	○	○	○	○	○	○
Sunday	○	○	○	○	○	○	○	○	○	○	○	○	○	○	○	○	○	○	○	○	○	○	○	○

Mood

MON
TUE
WED
THU
FRI
SAT
SUN

Daily Water Log

MON
TUES
WED
THU
FRI
SAT
SUN

Weekly Tally & Notes

Body Measurements:

BUST _____
UPPER ARM _____
WAIST _____
HIPS _____
UPPER LEG _____

bust _____
upper arm _____
waist _____
hips _____
upper leg _____

Weekly Weight Tracker

CURRENT WEIGHT _____
GOAL WEIGHT _____

STRUGGLES

VICTORIES

Notes:

Your only limit is you.

Daily Fasting Tracker

	1AM	2AM	3AM	4AM	5AM	6AM	7AM	8AM	9AM	10AM	11AM	12PM	1PM	2PM	3PM	4PM	5PM	6PM	7PM	8PM	9PM	10PM	11PM	12AM
Monday	○	○	○	○	○	○	○	○	○	○	○	○	○	○	○	○	○	○	○	○	○	○	○	○
Tuesday	○	○	○	○	○	○	○	○	○	○	○	○	○	○	○	○	○	○	○	○	○	○	○	○
Wednesday	○	○	○	○	○	○	○	○	○	○	○	○	○	○	○	○	○	○	○	○	○	○	○	○
Thursday	○	○	○	○	○	○	○	○	○	○	○	○	○	○	○	○	○	○	○	○	○	○	○	○
Friday	○	○	○	○	○	○	○	○	○	○	○	○	○	○	○	○	○	○	○	○	○	○	○	○
Saturday	○	○	○	○	○	○	○	○	○	○	○	○	○	○	○	○	○	○	○	○	○	○	○	○
Sunday	○	○	○	○	○	○	○	○	○	○	○	○	○	○	○	○	○	○	○	○	○	○	○	○

Mood

MON
TUE
WED
THU
FRI
SAT
SUN

Daily Water Log

MON	◇ ◇ ◇ ◇ ◇ ◇ ◇ ◇
TUES	◇ ◇ ◇ ◇ ◇ ◇ ◇ ◇
WED	◇ ◇ ◇ ◇ ◇ ◇ ◇ ◇
THU	◇ ◇ ◇ ◇ ◇ ◇ ◇ ◇
FRI	◇ ◇ ◇ ◇ ◇ ◇ ◇ ◇
SAT	◇ ◇ ◇ ◇ ◇ ◇ ◇ ◇
SUN	◇ ◇ ◇ ◇ ◇ ◇ ◇ ◇

Weekly Tally & Notes

Body Measurements:

BUST _____
UPPER ARM _____
WAIST _____
HIPS _____
UPPER LEG _____

bust _____
upper arm _____
waist _____
hips _____
upper leg _____

Weekly Weight Tracker

CURRENT WEIGHT _____
GOAL WEIGHT _____

STRUGGLES

VICTORIES

Notes:

Inhale the future, exhale the past.

Daily Fasting Tracker

	1AM	2AM	3AM	4AM	5AM	6AM	7AM	8AM	9AM	10AM	11AM	12PM	1PM	2PM	3PM	4PM	5PM	6PM	7PM	8PM	9PM	10PM	11PM	12AM
Monday	○	○	○	○	○	○	○	○	○	○	○	○	○	○	○	○	○	○	○	○	○	○	○	○
Tuesday	○	○	○	○	○	○	○	○	○	○	○	○	○	○	○	○	○	○	○	○	○	○	○	○
Wednesday	○	○	○	○	○	○	○	○	○	○	○	○	○	○	○	○	○	○	○	○	○	○	○	○
Thursday	○	○	○	○	○	○	○	○	○	○	○	○	○	○	○	○	○	○	○	○	○	○	○	○
Friday	○	○	○	○	○	○	○	○	○	○	○	○	○	○	○	○	○	○	○	○	○	○	○	○
Saturday	○	○	○	○	○	○	○	○	○	○	○	○	○	○	○	○	○	○	○	○	○	○	○	○
Sunday	○	○	○	○	○	○	○	○	○	○	○	○	○	○	○	○	○	○	○	○	○	○	○	○

Mood

MON
TUE
WED
THU
FRI
SAT
SUN

Daily Water Log

MON
TUES
WED
THU
FRI
SAT
SUN

Weekly Tally & Notes

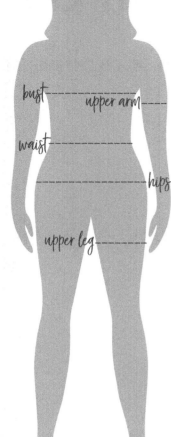

bust
upper arm
waist
hips
upper leg

Body Measurements:

BUST _____
UPPER ARM _____
WAIST _____
HIPS _____
UPPER LEG _____

Weekly Weight Tracker

CURRENT WEIGHT _____
GOAL WEIGHT _____

Notes:

STRUGGLES

VICTORIES

Strive for progress not perfection.

Daily Fasting Tracker

	1AM	2AM	3AM	4AM	5AM	6AM	7AM	8AM	9AM	10AM	11AM	12PM	1PM	2PM	3PM	4PM	5PM	6PM	7PM	8PM	9PM	10PM	11PM	12AM
Monday	○	○	○	○	○	○	○	○	○	○	○	○	○	○	○	○	○	○	○	○	○	○	○	○
Tuesday	○	○	○	○	○	○	○	○	○	○	○	○	○	○	○	○	○	○	○	○	○	○	○	○
Wednesday	○	○	○	○	○	○	○	○	○	○	○	○	○	○	○	○	○	○	○	○	○	○	○	○
Thursday	○	○	○	○	○	○	○	○	○	○	○	○	○	○	○	○	○	○	○	○	○	○	○	○
Friday	○	○	○	○	○	○	○	○	○	○	○	○	○	○	○	○	○	○	○	○	○	○	○	○
Saturday	○	○	○	○	○	○	○	○	○	○	○	○	○	○	○	○	○	○	○	○	○	○	○	○
Sunday	○	○	○	○	○	○	○	○	○	○	○	○	○	○	○	○	○	○	○	○	○	○	○	○

Mood

MON
TUE
WED
THU
FRI
SAT
SUN

Daily Water Log

MON
TUES
WED
THU
FRI
SAT
SUN

Weekly Tally & Notes

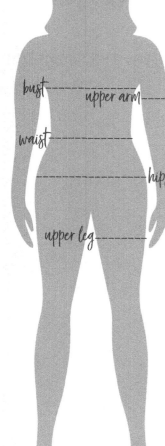

bust ———
upper arm ———
waist ———
hips
upper leg ———

Body Measurements:

BUST _____
UPPER ARM _____
WAIST _____
HIPS _____
UPPER LEG _____

Weekly Weight Tracker

CURRENT WEIGHT _____
GOAL WEIGHT _____

STRUGGLES

VICTORIES

Notes:

You are what you do, not what you say you'll do.

Daily Fasting Tracker

	1AM	2AM	3AM	4AM	5AM	6AM	7AM	8AM	9AM	10AM	11AM	12PM	1PM	2PM	3PM	4PM	5PM	6PM	7PM	8PM	9PM	10PM	11PM	12AM
Monday	○	○	○	○	○	○	○	○	○	○	○	○	○	○	○	○	○	○	○	○	○	○	○	○
Tuesday	○	○	○	○	○	○	○	○	○	○	○	○	○	○	○	○	○	○	○	○	○	○	○	○
Wednesday	○	○	○	○	○	○	○	○	○	○	○	○	○	○	○	○	○	○	○	○	○	○	○	○
Thursday	○	○	○	○	○	○	○	○	○	○	○	○	○	○	○	○	○	○	○	○	○	○	○	○
Friday	○	○	○	○	○	○	○	○	○	○	○	○	○	○	○	○	○	○	○	○	○	○	○	○
Saturday	○	○	○	○	○	○	○	○	○	○	○	○	○	○	○	○	○	○	○	○	○	○	○	○
Sunday	○	○	○	○	○	○	○	○	○	○	○	○	○	○	○	○	○	○	○	○	○	○	○	○

Mood

MON
TUE
WED
THU
FRI
SAT
SUN

Daily Water Log

MON
TUES
WED
THU
FRI
SAT
SUN

Weekly Tally & Notes

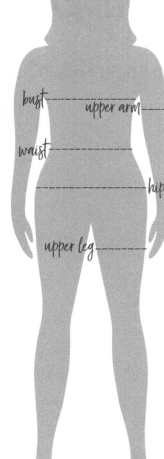

bust
upper arm
waist
hips
upper leg

Body Measurements:

BUST _____
UPPER ARM _____
WAIST _____
HIPS _____
UPPER LEG _____

Weekly Weight Tracker

CURRENT WEIGHT _____
GOAL WEIGHT _____

STRUGGLES

VICTORIES

Notes:

You get what you work for, not what you wish for.

Daily Fasting Tracker

	1AM	2AM	3AM	4AM	5AM	6AM	7AM	8AM	9AM	10AM	11AM	12PM	1PM	2PM	3PM	4PM	5PM	6PM	7PM	8PM	9PM	10PM	11PM	12AM
Monday	○	○	○	○	○	○	○	○	○	○	○	○	○	○	○	○	○	○	○	○	○	○	○	○
Tuesday	○	○	○	○	○	○	○	○	○	○	○	○	○	○	○	○	○	○	○	○	○	○	○	○
Wednesday	○	○	○	○	○	○	○	○	○	○	○	○	○	○	○	○	○	○	○	○	○	○	○	○
Thursday	○	○	○	○	○	○	○	○	○	○	○	○	○	○	○	○	○	○	○	○	○	○	○	○
Friday	○	○	○	○	○	○	○	○	○	○	○	○	○	○	○	○	○	○	○	○	○	○	○	○
Saturday	○	○	○	○	○	○	○	○	○	○	○	○	○	○	○	○	○	○	○	○	○	○	○	○
Sunday	○	○	○	○	○	○	○	○	○	○	○	○	○	○	○	○	○	○	○	○	○	○	○	○

Mood

Daily Water Log

MON	○ ○ ○ ○ ○ ○ ○ ○
TUES	○ ○ ○ ○ ○ ○ ○ ○
WED	○ ○ ○ ○ ○ ○ ○ ○
THU	○ ○ ○ ○ ○ ○ ○ ○
FRI	○ ○ ○ ○ ○ ○ ○ ○
SAT	○ ○ ○ ○ ○ ○ ○ ○
SUN	○ ○ ○ ○ ○ ○ ○ ○

Weekly Tally & Notes

Body Measurements:

BUST _____
UPPER ARM _____
WAIST _____
HIPS _____
UPPER LEG _____

Weekly Weight Tracker

CURRENT WEIGHT _____
GOAL WEIGHT _____

Notes:

bust _____
upper arm _____
waist _____
hips _____
upper leg _____

STRUGGLES

VICTORIES

It doesn't get easier. You just get stronger.

Daily Fasting Tracker

	1AM	2AM	3AM	4AM	5AM	6AM	7AM	8AM	9AM	10AM	11AM	12PM	1PM	2PM	3PM	4PM	5PM	6PM	7PM	8PM	9PM	10PM	11PM	12AM
Monday	○	○	○	○	○	○	○	○	○	○	○	○	○	○	○	○	○	○	○	○	○	○	○	○
Tuesday	○	○	○	○	○	○	○	○	○	○	○	○	○	○	○	○	○	○	○	○	○	○	○	○
Wednesday	○	○	○	○	○	○	○	○	○	○	○	○	○	○	○	○	○	○	○	○	○	○	○	○
Thursday	○	○	○	○	○	○	○	○	○	○	○	○	○	○	○	○	○	○	○	○	○	○	○	○
Friday	○	○	○	○	○	○	○	○	○	○	○	○	○	○	○	○	○	○	○	○	○	○	○	○
Saturday	○	○	○	○	○	○	○	○	○	○	○	○	○	○	○	○	○	○	○	○	○	○	○	○
Sunday	○	○	○	○	○	○	○	○	○	○	○	○	○	○	○	○	○	○	○	○	○	○	○	○

Mood

MON
TUE
WED
THU
FRI
SAT
SUN

Daily Water Log

MON
TUES
WED
THU
FRI
SAT
SUN

Weekly Tally & Notes

Body Measurements:

BUST _____
UPPER ARM _____
WAIST _____
HIPS _____
UPPER LEG _____

Weekly Weight Tracker

CURRENT WEIGHT _____
GOAL WEIGHT _____

STRUGGLES

VICTORIES

Notes:

bust

upper arm

waist

hips

upper leg

Let your dreams be your wings.

Daily Fasting Tracker

	1AM	2AM	3AM	4AM	5AM	6AM	7AM	8AM	9AM	10AM	11AM	12PM	1PM	2PM	3PM	4PM	5PM	6PM	7PM	8PM	9PM	10PM	11PM	12AM
Monday	○	○	○	○	○	○	○	○	○	○	○	○	○	○	○	○	○	○	○	○	○	○	○	○
Tuesday	○	○	○	○	○	○	○	○	○	○	○	○	○	○	○	○	○	○	○	○	○	○	○	○
Wednesday	○	○	○	○	○	○	○	○	○	○	○	○	○	○	○	○	○	○	○	○	○	○	○	○
Thursday	○	○	○	○	○	○	○	○	○	○	○	○	○	○	○	○	○	○	○	○	○	○	○	○
Friday	○	○	○	○	○	○	○	○	○	○	○	○	○	○	○	○	○	○	○	○	○	○	○	○
Saturday	○	○	○	○	○	○	○	○	○	○	○	○	○	○	○	○	○	○	○	○	○	○	○	○
Sunday	○	○	○	○	○	○	○	○	○	○	○	○	○	○	○	○	○	○	○	○	○	○	○	○

Mood

MON
TUE
WED
THU
FRI
SAT
SUN

Daily Water Log

MON	◇ ◇ ◇ ◇ ◇ ◇ ◇ ◇
TUES	◇ ◇ ◇ ◇ ◇ ◇ ◇ ◇
WED	◇ ◇ ◇ ◇ ◇ ◇ ◇ ◇
THU	◇ ◇ ◇ ◇ ◇ ◇ ◇ ◇
FRI	◇ ◇ ◇ ◇ ◇ ◇ ◇ ◇
SAT	◇ ◇ ◇ ◇ ◇ ◇ ◇ ◇
SUN	◇ ◇ ◇ ◇ ◇ ◇ ◇ ◇

Weekly Tally & Notes

Body Measurements:

BUST _____
UPPER ARM _____
WAIST _____
HIPS _____
UPPER LEG _____

bust _____
upper arm _____
waist _____
hips _____
upper leg _____

Weekly Weight Tracker

CURRENT WEIGHT _____
GOAL WEIGHT _____

STRUGGLES

VICTORIES

Notes:

Find joy in the journey.

Daily Fasting Tracker

	1AM	2AM	3AM	4AM	5AM	6AM	7AM	8AM	9AM	10AM	11AM	12PM	1PM	2PM	3PM	4PM	5PM	6PM	7PM	8PM	9PM	10PM	11PM	12AM
Monday	○	○	○	○	○	○	○	○	○	○	○	○	○	○	○	○	○	○	○	○	○	○	○	○
Tuesday	○	○	○	○	○	○	○	○	○	○	○	○	○	○	○	○	○	○	○	○	○	○	○	○
Wednesday	○	○	○	○	○	○	○	○	○	○	○	○	○	○	○	○	○	○	○	○	○	○	○	○
Thursday	○	○	○	○	○	○	○	○	○	○	○	○	○	○	○	○	○	○	○	○	○	○	○	○
Friday	○	○	○	○	○	○	○	○	○	○	○	○	○	○	○	○	○	○	○	○	○	○	○	○
Saturday	○	○	○	○	○	○	○	○	○	○	○	○	○	○	○	○	○	○	○	○	○	○	○	○
Sunday	○	○	○	○	○	○	○	○	○	○	○	○	○	○	○	○	○	○	○	○	○	○	○	○

Mood

MON
TUE
WED
THU
FRI
SAT
SUN

Daily Water Log

MON
TUES
WED
THU
FRI
SAT
SUN

Weekly Tally & Notes

Body Measurements:

BUST _____
UPPER ARM _____
WAIST _____
HIPS _____
UPPER LEG _____

Weekly Weight Tracker

CURRENT WEIGHT _____
GOAL WEIGHT _____

STRUGGLES

VICTORIES

Notes:

The best view comes after the hardest climb.

Year in Review

STARTING WEIGHT

ENDING WEIGHT

TOTAL WEIGHT LOST

TOTAL INCHES LOST

GREATEST STRUGGLE

GREATEST VICTORY

DID YOU MEET YOUR GOAL

WHAT IS YOUR NEXT GOAL

Congrats on completing an entire year of Intermittent Fasting!

Made in the USA
Monee, IL
11 November 2021